The Aurora

Jim Henderson AMPA, ARPS is a Scottish professional photographer living on Deeside in Aberdeenshire. He has built up a specialist collection from photographing over 120 Auroras since 1989. He gives regular illustrated talks on the Aurora and has written many articles published both locally and in national photography magazines.

John MacNicol (President of Aberdeen and District Astronomical Society for fifteen years) is a Lecturer in Astronomy and currently works in the international oil exploration industry as a software support analyst.

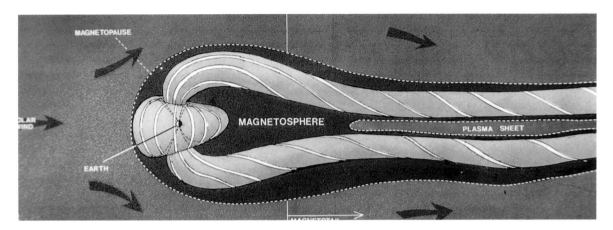

These two photographs, taken from some excellent coloured displays in the City Observatory, Edinburgh, were offered to me for this book by the Observatory Director, James Shepherd. James was very instrumental in putting me on the path of photographing the night sky, having gone to much trouble to draw by hand the path of Halley's Comet in 1985/6 so that I could photograph it at all stages. He also provided detailed advice on how to photograph the comet, which I did successfully – it also proved good advice for the later Aurora work. At that time the idea was sown in my mind to try to photograph an Aurora – it happened at last in 1989.

I am delighted to be able to show two of the display paintings but saddened that they have to be in memory of the artist, Peter Cattell (1958–1997), a former Assistant Director of the City Observatory who died earlier this year in Newcastle, a highly skilled artist whose work in astronomy will be sorely missed.

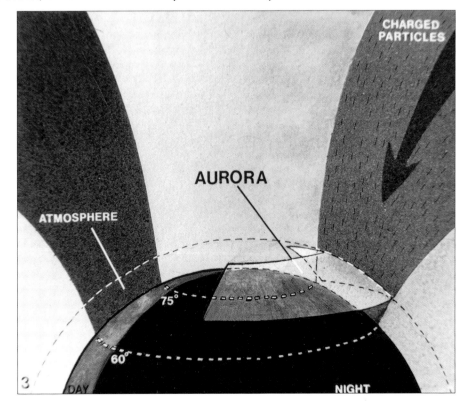

The Aurora

An Introduction for Observers and Photographers

Jim Henderson and John MacNicol

Foreword by Professor John C. Brown,
10th Astronomer Royal for Scotland

A catalogue record for this book is available
from the British Library.

ISBN 0 9529434 1 7

Design and typesetting by
XL Publishing Services, Lurley, Tiverton
Printed in Hong Kong
by Regent Publishing Services

CONTENTS

LIST OF COLOUR PLATES

NOTE ON THE COLOUR PLATES

Many of the colour photographs, especially the Author's based on the Fuji 1600 emulsion, give a very enhanced colour rendition and are not necessarily the way Aurora displays are seen by the ordinary human eye. The very red Corona's are often seen as the film records but many of the lower level displays appear as whitish in colour or a pale hue of the green or red.

The author's photographs are not noted as such but are those not otherwise designated. For the locations indicated for his photographs the following details should be noted:

Cairn O'Mount - hilltop in South East Grampian near Fettercairn.

The Neuk, The Ley and the Harestone Road are locations just to the East of Banchory on a road which goes around the North of Crathes Castle.

Crooktree is the author's current home and lies between the Deeside villages of Kincardine O'Neil and Torphins and is to the North of the River Dee, about 25 miles West of Aberdeen. All the times given on the author's captions are based on GMT.

FOREWORD

One of the unforgettable experiences of my life was on a flight home from Boston. I can rarely sleep on planes but, having already been 'on the road' for about 29 hours on the long way home from Sydney, I felt sure to conk out for the night. Then the pilot announced that to starboard was an auroral display and (for some reason I do not comprehend to this day) that we should look soon as it would only be visible for a short time. In fact it simply got better and better as the night deepened and as we headed north. Although I had seen the Aurora occasionally from the Glasgow area, this presented a whole new world for me even through the poky plane windows illuminated by the inside glow of the usual awful airline movie. Not quite in the league of the view from orbit, I dare say, but the ever changing shapes and colours of this splendid natural light show in the dark sky at 12km above the curving horizon is as near as I will get to a view from space of these wonderful events. What has stuck in my mind as much as the vision itself was my conversation with the Captain later in the flight. When I urged him to announce this once in a lifetime opportunity again he agreed that it was very impressive, almost inducing vertigo in the cockpit team, but that "a lot of people are asleep or watching the movie, and we still have to do the Duty Free sales" So much then for the wonders of Nature!!

To go through life never having seen an auroral display would be a great loss, the more so for those of us living at high enough latitude to have the good fortune to have the opportunity. Quite a few of my astronomer colleagues have in fact never done so, partly because many of them are theorists rather than observers but also because they share the myth that Aurorae are rare and hard to observe. With the publication of this lovely little book, Jim Henderson and John MacNicol do us all a great service in a number of ways. First of all they dispel this myth. Second, they tell us how to maximise our chances of observing Aurorae often and to best advantage, and how to photograph them. And thirdly, for those too lazy, or "too busy" enjoying our Duty Free, they provide us with a truly fantastic collection of colour photographs of the Aurora in all its splendour to keep as inspiration on our coffee tables. These should inspire many to go out and look for themselves and some to take on the addictive challenge of regular fishing to obtain ever better photographs. I have never done this myself but

spring 1996 evaporated for me in the similar mania of photographing Comet Hale-Bopp which features on these pages alongside the Aurora. (One of our postgraduate students, Aidan Keane, won a departmental competition for his Hale-Bopp photo from the Glasgow area featuring an Aurora on the same night.)

The style of this book makes it highly accessible to all, written with authority but also with simplicity and clarity both in describing how to observe and photograph our Northern Lights and in their physical origins. Like comets, the Aurora shines by atomic processes akin to fluorescent lights excited by the emissions – plasma, particles and light – from the Sun. The detailed processes involved in solar activity and in the Aurora are still not well understood, involving the complex physics of magnetised plasmas (which coincidentally I had been working on in Sydney). Progress towards such understanding is aided by the regular collection of data and photographs, much of it by dedicated scientific amateurs. The very fine collection of images on the following pages can therefore serve as inspiration for others to contribute to this research. Among the many important innovative techniques undertaken by amateurs is stereo imaging of the Aurora by use of widely separated cameras – a technique which impressed me greatly when I saw it at the 1996 Scottish Astronomers Weekend at Calton Hill, Edinburgh, along with stereo images of Comet Hyakutake using the earth's rotation to obtain separated viewpoints.

Studying Aurorae is not only important for their intrinsic scientific interest but also because of their links to phenomena of everyday significance such as the disruption of telecommunications and even the destruction of power supply elements through the effects of geomagnetic storms induced by solar activity. So I urge all purchasers of this unique volume to get out there and join the observers who can contribute to this scientific endeavour or, at the very least, to appreciate the efforts of others while simply enjoying some of the beautiful images they have so patiently acquired and made available here for all.

Professor John C. Brown, DSc, FRSE, FInstP
10th Astronomer Royal for Scotland
University of Glasgow

ACKNOWLEDGEMENTS

GENERAL ACKNOWLEDGEMENTS

In the preparation of any book there are many people who have been involved at various levels, from giving general moral support to those who have contributed in constructive and practical ways. To all those I would extend my gratitude but there are some I would wish to mention by name.

Firstly to John who has not only contributed as my co-author, but who has been a stalwart friend over the years answering my never ending stream of questions about the Aurora and computers. He has also stayed with me through nearly thirty rejections from various publishers in his support for our common wish that this book had to be published. Equally supportive of this 'dream', in the form of a book, have been Alison Leslie and Roger Thorp from the 'trade' who never once through all the trials ever advised me to give up. I hope the eventual sales of this book prove their assessment to be the right one. Also to a very dear friend, Elizabeth Garrard in Savannah, Georgia who has had to wait as long as me to see the book eventually be realised.

In terms of the book, a great debt of gratitude has to go to Professor John Brown, the Scottish Astronomer Royal, for his most cherished and generous Foreword. In addition I must thank David Gavine along with that of Ron Livesey, both well known for their major role in the British Aurora scene, for their time in reviewing the technical correctness of both of the authors' writings.

I would wish to make special mention of Robert Adams, the farmer at the Neuk, who tolerated my nocturnal visits on his land for many years and to my present landlord, Andrew Bradford, for giving me the chance to have my second ideal Aurora-viewing site and a lovely home as well.

Mention must be made of those who have had a practical hand in helping with the book; my cousin Kate in Melbourne who tracked down Martin in Tasmania and gave up valuable time from doing her animations; Janet Dalrymple at the Geophysical Institute at the University of Alaska for coming up with the selection of NASA and Alaskan Auroras; Lynda (at last) and Shirley for wading through my writing and sifting it for the many flaws of expression and spelling; lastly to Gordon Beckwith for steering me so professionally through the pitfalls of publishing and to Grant Shipcott for taking the rough outlines of the idea and giving it form and such wonderful visual substance.

My last and very special thanks has to go to Lillian, John's wife, who has answered the telephone with a patience and charm that never made me ever feel like the 'pain' I must have been; I have not worked it out but since I started photographing the Aurora in 1989 it must have been nearly a thousand times. She is not taken for granted.

Jim Henderson, Crooktree August 1997

PHOTOGRAPHIC ACKNOWLEDGEMENTS

The author wishes to express his great thanks to those people who have kindly taken the trouble to send him several of their photographs to consider and use in this book, as well as the additional assistance and advice they have graciously extended and they are:

Jay Brausch of Glen Ullin, North Dakota, USA; David Gavine, Edinburgh, Scotland; Martin George, Launceston Planetarium, Hobart, Tasmania, Australia; Steve Graham, Aberdeen, Scotland; David Huestis, Rhode Island, USA; Clive Johnson FRGS, Clive Johnson Picture Library, Buxton; John MacNicol, Kemnay, Scotland; Tom McEwan, Ayrshire; R. Overmyer, NASA -Spacelab 111/Challenger; Pekka Parviainen, Polar Image, Turku, Finland; Richard Pearce, Elgin, Moray, Scotland; Brian Sidney, Cramlington, Northumberland, England.; Lee Snyder, Geophysical Institute, University of Alaska, Fairbanks.

THE AURORA BOREALIS

The *Aurora Borealis* is a naturally occurring display of lights seen usually in the Northern Hemisphere night sky. They can occur at anytime of the year but are only seen with the human eye during the hours of darkness whenever that might be given the seasonal factors involved eg after 6.00pm in December but only after 11.00pm in late April or early September. An experienced observer could see them at twilight when the high rays can be enhanced by UV radiation from the Sun. They are not usually seen in the mid-summer months because the level of background light is too strong.

The Aurora light displays are caused by charged particles, thrown from emissions on the surface of the Sun into space and which are carried on the solar winds in any direction. Some of these particles reach the outer regions of the Earth and are 'captured' by the magnetic belts which surround the outer atmosphere of the Earth. These particles are then guided into the Earth's atmosphere at the two Polar Regions where they collide with the gas molecules floating freely in the upper areas of the Earth's atmosphere; they excite the gas molecules they collide with, causing them to glow in the way in which a neon or fluorescent tube does.

This light effect occurs anything from about 70 to 300 miles up in the Earth's atmosphere and it is this enormous scale that makes the Aurora display so spectacular. The movements of the display are equally enormous in their scale and it is these two characteristics that make the Aurora so different, and in a sense so obvious when you see it occurring in the night sky. There are some predictable patterns that occur in the shape, colour and movements of the Auroral display and later descriptions will allow the observer to distinguish the Aurora from any other night-time light displays from lightning to the rabbit-shooting spotlight sweeping back and forth behind the distant hill-line.

The *Aurora Borealis* is the description for these light displays which happen in the Northern skies but are described as the *Aurora Australis* when they occur in the South Pole regions of the world (see Plates 77/78). They are also known as the Northern Lights - those of the famous song associated with the city of Aberdeen on the North East coast of Scotland although there is some argument that these 'lights' are those of the Old Aberdeen seen by returning fishermen. They have also been called the Merry Dancers or the Heavenly Dancers, this particularly referring to the often frenzied and very active nature of the light displays.

The Aurora displays can be linked with different types of events that occur on the Sun's surface from the so called Sunspots, solar flares as well as other surface disturbances. The reasons for these happenings on the Sun's surface are not fully understood although much scientific effort is expended trying to explain and understand what is seen happening through telescopes and satellite studies. The most common Sun event that is known eventually to bring about auroral displays is that called Sunspots - these are black dots that appear on the Sun's surface, travelling from East to West over a period of days. The Sunspots have been observed to follow a pattern of activity from frequent to quiet every eleven years or so and it is when the Sunspots are around their most frequent that the greatest Aurora activity has been recorded.

The most spectacular of the photographs reproduced in this book and those referring to Corona displays are taken from the recent high frequency part of the eleven year cycle which occurred around 1989–1992. The next peak of the cycle will thus be around the year 2000 although we can expect a pick up of auroral activity in the years preceding that date. There are however auroral displays every year, even during the quieter period of the eleven-year cycle as evidenced by the photographs of the display on 7 March 1994. These less frequent, and not always very spectacular or colourful displays, maybe caused by the occasional Sunspot or possibly other more random disturbances on the Sun's surface.

This has been a very brief introduction to the Aurora which I hope will be sufficient for those seeking to proceed further with my more general observations of them in the next few pages.If you wish to delve more deeply into an understanding of the Aurora - the historical perspective, the science and astronomy of them then please read John's sections (page 72).

HOW TO SEE THE AURORA

I have already suggested that the Aurora can only be seen during the hours of darkness and in the main that is the basic requirement. A further necessity is that the night sky needs to be free from cloud - so if you can see the stars then you will see an auroral display if it is there. The North East of Scotland where I have studied the Aurora is a reasonably good area from which to observe them. I have seen well in excess of 100 displays since 1989.During the most active period this amounted to an average of one a month with a display frequency of two to three nights in a row at best, one night at worst. Cloud can unfortunately be a problem and often displays can be glimpsed only through passing gaps in the cloud cover with all the frustrations that that can bring.

The second necessity for seeing Aurora is the most obvious – you need to be outside (or able to see clearly outside) on a regular basis. The keen dog-walkers, rabbit shooters (poachers?) and astronomers, or travellers driving north from Edinburgh theatre shows are probably those most likely to spot auroral displays – those merry few walking home from hostelries might have seen auroral displays but either won't have worked out the differences in the night sky or will not remember next morning what they thought they saw!

I have seen plenty of Auroras because I have eccentric nocturnal habits and spend most evenings – especially clear starry ones – dashing out to check periodically to see if anything is there. It is not however quite the heavy commitment that I am suggesting as auroral displays occur as part of a build up of activity in the upper atmosphere and there are early indications of this – the Auroral Glow and the Arc in particular.

THE AURORAL GLOW

During the nights when there are no auroral displays imminent the dark sky is generally of a uniform light level disrupted perhaps by the reflected glow from local villages or a nearby city. This is most noticeable when there is a low cloud level and this yellowish glow shines on the clouds on the horizon line directly over the artificial lights in question.

When looking for auroral displays it is important to know where these street lights or even security lights from farms or other large buildings might be, particularly those in a northerly direction – the direction from where the Aurora is most likely to occur. In the case of those living along the Moray Firth or in the Shetland and Orkney Islands, a clear view over the sea is less likely to suffer from the confusion of man-made light pollution.

The Auroral Glow is however often a precursor of a build-up of charged-particles in the atmosphere and it is distinguishable as a general overall lightness – very pale whitish glow – in the northern sky where there should normally be expected to be a uniform darkness. This glow is similar to the last vestiges of twilight but is not, as it will be seen to be occurring long after twilight should be expected to have died away. Watching the sky and getting to know its general characteristics is an important

step in identifying Aurora displays. See Plate 2.

The human eye's response to dark light is important to know as well and it is usually necessary to allow time – 15–30mins for the eye to adjust to the low light conditions. Looking outside immediately after watching television, playing on the computer or being in a brightly lit room will mean that your eyes will not be sensitised to the low light conditions and the low level auroral light might be missed – you will see a major display however even if just going outside for a few minutes and it will grow brighter the longer the time is spent watching it.

I have often found that this distinct glow can last for one or two nights before the Aurora itself appears – at other times this distinct lightness of the night sky can lead to nothing happening at all. It is a general indicator only but is one of the most useful clues of a possible build up to a display.

Sometimes the magnetic interference of the radio airwaves, due to the bombardment of these charged particles, can be forewarned on TV or radio broadcasts although in practice I have never seen an auroral display when such a warning has been given. Astronomers can measure magnetic disturbances using a magnetometer and this can also, though not always, indicate the likelihood of possible auroral displays. My success in seeing them has come mainly from dogged perseverance and luck!

THE AURORAL ARC

The first real sign of an auroral display is the early build up of charged activity called the Arc. The arc is often the earliest sign of a display and is so called because of the shape it takes in the northern sky lying like a flat rainbow – a low curve of usually silvery white light – from east to west starting just above the horizon line. The arc is a very distinct shape and is not difficult to see and when it is seen it will very obvious – this bright band of light against the dark night sky. Stars will be seen above and beneath it. It can at times be so bright that the underneath looks dark enough that it could be mistaken for a distant hill line. See Plates 3 to 5.

The arc will often last for several hours, and the degree of brightness will change during that period, sometimes almost disappearing to a point that you questioned whether having seen it at all. If this happens do not give up – it will appear again in a few minutes time and this sequence of appearing and fading can last for an hour or a whole evening; unfortunately though rarely this distinct arc can be active all evening but never ever reaching a point where an active auroral display occurs; that is a very frustrating evening – like fishing all day without a bite!

If a particularly powerful display is on the cards, the arc will gradually intensify in brightness and occasionally a colour hue, often green, will become apparent. As the arc builds so too does its height and the low band will climb higher in the night sky. On occasions this powerful band will split in two and two bands will appear rather like a double rainbow and certainly then, the expectation is for a very active auroral display to be imminent; that is not the moment to go inside to put the kettle on. The change from a bright strong arc to the display starting can be a matter of seconds although I have noticed over several displays that the point of an active display starting often just follows an apparent fading of the strong arc. The active display usually leads with the flaring off of Rays which give the appearance of beams of light climbing upwards from the surface of the arc and this is the next most common stage.

THE AURORAL RAY

The Ray is probably the most common shape of an auroral display that people will see in this area of Scotland, eg the North East. Single or multiple rays are seen in the night sky stretching upwards not just from the distinct base of an arc but often appearing from some point in the sky above and below the horizon line. See Plates 6 to 9.

The rays also exhibit much of the activity associated with Aurora displays and because of these two characteristics – height and movement are often the auroral elements first spotted by the unaccustomed eye. The single ray is often mistaken for car headlights which can be seen sweeping across a hilly outline as the car proceeds up a road on the far side of the hill. The best way to distinguish between them is to watch them carefully – the car lights tend to disappear completely or come into view as the car comes over the hill; the auroral ray will tend to stay more static, in one place and continue for several seconds up to a couple of minutes shining upwards into the night sky like a searchlight. If it moves sideways, which it frequently does, it tends to move along an axis rather as if someone was pushing one of the old World War 2-type searchlights along a low bridge on a trolley. When there are several rays in an active display then there is usually no difficulty in realising what they are: as I always tell people – if you see an auroral display then you will be in no doubt as to what it is – there is nothing to compare with one.

In most cases the auroral rays lean towards the left – or east to west, and mostly they travel in that direction, although I have seen them moving in the other direction as well. When they are particularly powerful they can stretch upwards to a point almost above the viewer sometimes reaching the height of the Pole Star and it is on these occasions that colours tend to be more visible. The more usual colour of the Aurora is silvery white with hues of green. I have tended to see red only when the display appears to grow in strength as for instance with a Corona developing. See Plates 26 & 38 for examples.

Multi-coloured Aurora are much rarer at our latitudes and these I will describe in more detail under the heading of Corona. The light level of an Aurora is very low so the sensitivity of the human eye to them is poor. The colours of many of these photographs are far beyond those discernible by the human eye and in most cases when I photographed these displays the colours where not visible other than as silvery white or yellow with the occasional hint of a colour usually green.

If there is a double arc, it seems that the rays become active at first off the lower arc and then the rays pass through the upper arc which in turn breaks up and produces its own rays and they then blend in together as the discharge continues. The length of time that passes as these rays occur can vary enormously from a few seconds to several minutes - generally though the rays last a minute or two before fading and then another one starts up and so on for ten to twenty minutes. The whole display will then fade away often to the point that there might never have been anything in the northern night sky other than the stars. Twenty to thirty minutes later another arc may start to appear and immediately in one or two hours the whole process will repeat itself again; this can go on all evening eventually dying out after midnight.

Some displays will remain in an active state for longer periods of time early in the evening, fading after an hour or two with nothing happening again until late evening or midnight and then only giving a short burst of activity before fading away totally. Particularly during the low activity period many of the displays, while not only being of a very low quality, also only lasted for a very short period with only a single or two rays visible. On the next occasion the single rays, so faint as to be hardly discernible, seemed to continue on for an hour or more appearing either from below the horizon or just as suddenly in the upper half of the sky.

The Rays do occasionally occur as a single very well defined beam, rather like a single searchlight although the only one that I have seen occurred on a very wet and cloudy evening and while it lasted for several minutes it came from no identifiable arc. It had all the features of a strong spotlight seeming to start several degrees up into the sky and then as abruptly ceasing at its upper point. That it wasn't a spotlight was confirmed by it being seen in the same position by an observer several miles west of my position – he had seen it to his left – to the West as well; later I heard of others who had seen it in other parts of the country. I had been out looking for an Aurora following early signs from the night before and it is most likely that this one appeared as it did through a clearing in the cloud base. Normally single rays occur as part of an evening's display in which many single rays are seen. See Plate 8.

The other rays that sometimes occur are referred to as appearing in a 'rayed band' as against the 'rayed arc' which is most common. The rayed band is less common in this area of Scotland as is the folding or kinked band – as against the arc type band. This folding band is far more common further north and is the commoner type of auroral structure seen in Alaska or Norway and is associated with the huge 'folding curtains' of auroral displays commonly associated with the Arctic or Antarctic explorers. See Plate 76.

FLAMING AND PATCHES ('STREAMERS')

These auroral displays tend to be less common but are seen perhaps with less powerful displays or those at the end of their active period.

The 'streamers', which is my personal description for what I have observed, are like unsuccessful rays smouldering along the arc rather like the way the glowing embers of a dying fire appear to move along sideways as the remnants burn out and then with that occasional intense flare-out of flame, appear to die for ever. These intense but small rays seem to be burning off as they move along the arc sometimes throwing up a small ray, bright yellow, very intense and lasting for only a short time before fading out, to then be replaced in another area when the process repeats itself again. See Plate 15.

Flaming seems to happen as the main display has died out although it is going on elsewhere below the northern horizon. In the distance, there seem to come flashes of light shooting upwards into the 'heavens' almost like the flashes of a military bombardment seen from far away. The flashes of light can be very regular at times in a pulsating sequence, more like the effect wind gusts have across a field of wheat or the surface of water in a loch, rather than the random one-off lightning flash, and they seem to flare up across the whole northern horizon from east to west as though some gigantic torch was being switched on and off again and again. They have been impossible to photograph. Another form of a similar light effect is that of 'flickering' which is usually seen only in the intense displays in the auroral zones and is a very rapid change of the brightness of the displays.

The other sort of 'flash' I have seen quite often is similar to lightning but more in the nature of the electric storm common in the Mediterranean. These are single flashes occurring usually towards the West but without any of the associated rumbles of thunder normally to be expected. These flashes generally occur with evenings of strong auroral glow; they are very random and do not occur often – three or four in an evening and always appearing to be far away over the horizon.

Patches can appear at the early, but more commonly later stages of an auroral display. They are just that – regular pulsating patches of faint light, often silvery white or of a pale bluish tinge which appear and disappear again as if several torches were being switched on and off; on occasions this aspect of a display has lasted for 15 or 20 minutes. On some evenings that is all I have seen, without any arc or larger display ever happening. See Plates 14 & 25.

THE CORONA

The Corona (or coronal rays) is the rarest of the auroral displays seen as far south as Northern Scotland. The Corona is best understood in terms of the nature of auroral displays; imagine a dough-ring deposited around the Earth and large enough to encircle the globe but with its starting point to the south of the Arctic ice-cap. This is the beginning of an Aurora display and as the charged particles are fed into this, it pushes southwards, stretching as it goes like a rubber band and getting broader as well. As the power level increases, it climbs higher into the upper atmosphere passing over the heads of the observers as it pushes on southwards. Instead of seeing those displays described earlier – mainly those north of us and which we are thus seeing as the 'front edge' of the main active area, we are now looking directly upwards and find that the rays are all around us dropping down to all the horizons regardless of what direction we might look. See Plates 17 to 23 and 30 in particular.

The sight that then confronts us is that all these rays are going from the centre point and dropping down to the horizon in any direction we care to look – the magnetic zenith, the point at the centre of the Corona and in Scotland several degrees south-east of the true magnetic zenith – appears almost directly above us giving the impression, for it is just that, that we are under some gigantic canopy like the dome of a cathedral. The rays are climbing several hundreds of miles into the upper atmosphere and although stretching straight upwards in great flat sheets from a point perhaps 70 miles above us, they appear to be bending inwards to this centre point.

It is on the occasions of the full or partial coronal display that I have seen different visible colours, particularly red and yellow, in February 1992 and in the case of the Corona over Crathes Castle in March 1991 it was the pastel hues of pink and green although earlier in the evening it started a deep red.

I remember seeing a multi-coloured Corona over Aboyne on 20 October 1989 but unfortunately I was unable to photograph it and by the time I got home and got my camera the cloud had moved in and I didn't see any more auroral display that night. I was on a newspaper assignment that evening so was able to drag the Aboyne Ladies Circle out from the Charleston Hotel to see it. In the case of that Corona there seemed to be all the colours of the rainbow visible moving in great bands up and down the many rays (or columns) of this many rayed 'dome'. I understand it was similar to the Great Aurora of March 1989 which kicked off the last Sunspot cycle peak.

On the rare occasions I have seen Coronas they seem to have started very early in the evening without any of the usual build up signs and for instance one on 26 February 1992 was a canopy of red everywhere when I went out at 7.00pm, although there had been nothing visible at 6.15pm when I first checked to see if there were any signs after darkness had established itself. My notes show that by 8.45pm it had clouded over completely and nothing further was to be seen all evening because of the cloud. See Plate 30.

A few days earlier, on 2 February, I had checked out on a cold and windy evening but could see nothing because of cloud and rain. However, John (co-author of this book) rang me around 10.45pm to say there was an active Aurora on the go; I went out immediately to find several rays which turned into a coronal crown over my house at 11.00pm with rays and curtains across the northern horizon from west to north east – this display continued until nearly 1.00am on the morning of the 3rd. See Plate 27.

WHERE TO SEE AURORAL DISPLAYS

Aurora Borealis displays occur generally in a band just south of the Arctic ice-cap; depending on their power level they can extend as far south as the south of England at latitude 50 although there have been historical sightings in Roman times of possible auroral displays near Rome around latitude 40. Displays in southern England are not as rare as usually perceived and the records kept by astronomers prove this, but the best opportunities to see Auroras in England are when we in Scotland are indulging in the full highly coloured coronal displays, which from my sightings are not all that common. See Plates 45 and 47.

I think that one of the first necessities for seeing auroral displays is to dispel the myth that they are very rare occurrences. They are however not all that common so there is in a sense little point spending hours sitting around hoping to see one. In practice that would be a wasted effort except for enthusiastic star-gazers who are spending much of their time on other night sky phenomena. The Aurora, as my own records show, occur very regularly and even when they are at their least active can still be seen several times a year. When there is a peak of the eleven-year Sunspot cycle then Aurora can be seen two or more times in a month, and displays can last over two or three nights in a row.

The interested observer will firstly identify a secluded site away from the light pollution of large towns and villages and which will give them a clear view to the North. If using some entrance to a field or similar area which is not of a public nature than it would be advisable to let the owner know the purpose of your regular nocturnal activities – it might save the embarrassment of a late night visitation from an Officer of the Law. It might be that the entrance is not always going to offer an uninterrupted view or maybe getting in the way of farming or forestry activities later in the year – just on the very evening you really didn't want to find your favourite spot filled by a combine harvester or forestry low-loader!

Although auroral displays usually take up plenty of the night sky stretching usually from East to West, I have always identified magnetic north and used a tree or particular shape on a hill line to mark its spot. This is a good starting reference point for sighting reports or initial photographs and allows you to build up a knowledge of that topography and any important light influences in that direction. My favourite site near Banchory is at the Neuk, on the plateau to the north of Crathes Castle, looking across to the Hill of Fare at its eastern end. On cloudy evenings light pollution from Westhill further to the right of that sighting point and sometimes Echt which was almost directly in front of me was very noticeable; this was not a problem on a clear night and didn't affect seeing Aurora displays but on nights of cloudy periods then this could pre-

A 24mm wide angle lens pointed at a January night sky and centred on the Pole Star allows the two most identifiable constellations - Cassiopeia (left) and The Plough or Ursa Major (right) - to be photographed together. These are good references for viewing Aurora displays in northern skies

sent problems of identifying low quality displays just visible through the gaps in the clouds. See Plate 24.

The other useful reference pointer for direction, and particularly for including in photographs for indicating scale as well as direction, is the stars. The three main bodies that I use throughout the season are the two easily identified constellations of *Ursa Major* (The Plough, The Great Bear or Big Dipper) - seven key stars which look like a large question mark - and *Cassiopeia*, five stars which are like a large letter 'W', and the third is the Pole Star itself. The two constellations move in a large circle round the Pole Star throughout the year. For those not very knowledgeable about the stars, those mentioned above are easily identified. See Plates 25 and 26 initially.

Astronomers tend to identify the direction and scale of auroral displays in terms of altitude and azimuths.

To acquaint yourselves with any of these pointers, firstly buy or borrow a compass, chose your intended viewpoint and take a reading for North - you will often be surprised just where it can be! After identifying North then look up into the winter night sky and in front of you or to your right will be the Plough like a large question mark and to your left will be *Cassiopeia*; between them and usually directly in front of you is the Pole Star.

The other major constellation which is of significance to include in a photograph of a Corona is Orion - include that in your photograph and you are looking almost South. The three centre stars gently sloping downwards from right to left are the key to identifying that constellation. See Plates 30 and 32.

One point in choosing a site is not to face oncoming traffic as this can make it difficult to maintain good night vision and is the worst thing for photography - car lights can burn out sensitive film very badly. This was a problem of a site I chose in my early days of photographing the Aurora - looking northwards from the top of the Cairn O'Mount (455m) - ideal for the height and uninterrupted vista but as the cars climbed up the route, even at 11.00pm at night, their headlights shone upwards into the void and left long gashes of light across the lower part of the photograph.

This also raises another point - keep your viewpoint as near to the North as you can practically make it. If you live in Grampian then I would not suggest going southwards, if you live in Banff or Buckie then great, just avoid the lights of offshore rigs tied up for repair or flashing harbour lights. Living in Aberdeen or Inverness should not necessarily be a problem for viewing the more powerful displays and the Aurora I photographed once directly from Banchory shows what can be seen and photographed, and that was even on a night of a full moon. See Plate 35. The problem of the big city is that it can be difficult to see the earlier stages of an Aurora, often very faint and low on the horizon and easily obscured by tall buildings and the general light levels. See Dave Gavine's Edinburgh study: Plate 65.

Watch the local press for reports of Aurora, especially during the peak times for although this means you may have missed a particular display it is a good indicator that they are on the go and others will be appearing later as I will now describe.

TIMING AURORA DISPLAYS

Auroral displays are not easily predictable. I have mentioned already the use of magnetometers but these tend to be accessible to the specialists only and media broadcasts of radio wave interference from magnetic storms but these in themselves are no guarantee of auroral light displays. During the last cycle I heard three announcements on the TV weather broadcasts about unusually high levels of magnetic disturbance but on neither occasion did I see any auroral displays on the nights in question.

In general terms auroral displays depend on the output of an emission from the Sun's surface throwing its charged particles in the direction of the Earth arriving some hours or days later in our vicinity - this in itself can be very much a hit or miss affair. Ideally the geomagnetic poles need to be directly in line with these incoming streams of electrons to give the best chance for the magnetic belts to 'catch' them and funnel them down into the upper atmosphere and then start the process which will end in Aurora displays. This best alignment happens approximately every 27 days or so and it is this relationship which is a useful but not a foolproof guide to timing likely displays.

Given this rough guide, a newspaper report of an auroral display could be a useful starting off point. In the next few years coming up to the millennium there should be increase in the displays and it will probably mean that with some diligence auroral displays will be observed almost to order and as the peak of the cycle is reached the frequency could be as much as two or three a month - that is when the addiction will begin!

Another aspect of timing auroral displays is the length of time they last. As I have already described under the section about the Arc this aspect of the early part of a display can last for several hours waxing and waning throughout the evening and on occasions doing nothing else - that is, never becoming active at all.

Once or twice it has apparently died out around mid evening, say 9.00pm, only to appear again at 11.00pm and eventually go active - ie start producing rays around 30 minutes later. More often the arc will appear in the early evening and after two or three sequences of waxing and waning will go active within the hour, and this pattern is then repeated throughout the evening culminating in a large display of rays and folding bands around midnight.

It is difficult to give exact timings for the lengths of displays but on average I have found 10 to 20 minutes seems to be the norm and it is a similar pattern to the waxing and waning period of the arc. Most average displays I have found had two really active periods with the strongest display occurring around midnight and then the whole process fading after that - on very few occasions did the auroral activity continue throughout the night. The longest I personally saw was the display on 30 April/1 May 1990 when the dawn light around 3.00am eventually overwhelmed the auroral display and it couldn't be seen anymore. During the active period of the cycle several displays continued after midnight but were of poorer quality with the rays getting fainter and more distant and usually I would leave the site around 1.30am in these cases.

The unpredictability of the displays is best illustrated by the one that occurred over Banchory on 11 April 1990. I had left the usual Crathes site at 11.30pm after seeing several strong rays even in the light from a full moon. Back at home again, I checked but I did not see anything very distinctive until the final look-see before bed at 1.30am (00.30 GMT) when I saw strong pulsating flashes which seemed to be getting stronger. See Plate 35.

I returned with the camera to find that they had changed into folds of blue light which very quickly gave off several large rays with a lot of movement, a rayed band - this continued for some 30 mins before finally dying out. This would however be the exception rather than the rule - generally, when I have checked later in the early hours of the morning I have usually found no further evidence of other activity.

ENVIRONMENTAL CONDITIONS

In this section I am referring to the weather conditions, temperatures and state of intruding natural light.

Over the years of observing Auroras I cannot say that I have identified any discernible pattern of conditions that I associate with the displays. The prerequisite is of course a cloud-free night and sufficient darkness to see the low level light displays - if one can see the stars shining distinctly then it is a good starting point.

I have photographed them in all kinds of weather conditions - cold, warm, windy, windless, rain or snow showers passing through, clear frosty nights to cloudy muggy ones. The most identifiable effect of the weather is on the degree or ease of visibility - on cloudy nights then the difficulty is spotting them through gaps in the clouds, or watching the displays disappear behind the cloak of evening mist as a change of temperature occurs or a snow shower spreads across and obliterates an arc just as it goes active; by the time the shower has passed the active stage has faded. Apart from the practicalities of photographing them, the weather conditions did not appear to affect the nature of the auroral display.

There have been suggestions that auroral displays follow or precede particular weather conditions but this may in fact be more coincidence than predictable fact. The complexity of the atmosphere, let alone the global weather patterns, probably makes such ideas no stronger than conjecture - it will be decades before science can create models allowing any sort of sophisticated prediction of the effects of solar particles on the weather on Earth. There is much research being undertaken and this is described in more detail in John's more technical section later in this book.

Light intrusion has already been touched on and it does have the most important role to play in seeing the Aurora. The artificial light pollution from street lights is becoming an increasing problem for astronomers throughout the world. Although steps can be taken to minimise such pollution without compromising the convenience to street users many councils do not appear to have a coherent policy in this field, and more likely would usually take the 'cheaper' option at first glance – though astronomers would argue that quite apart from the effect it was having on their activities it would often be more energy efficient in the long run to screen lights in the streets and make them more effective, and hence more efficient.

I have shown, especially with the photograph of Banchory (Plate 35), that Aurora are quite visible in extreme light conditions whether man-made or natural. Ron Livesey has told me that he has seen Aurora from both Edinburgh and Glasgow City centres (and see too the photograph by Steve taken in Aberdeen). See Plates 37, 64 and 65.

Moonlight is perhaps the strongest natural 'night' light that causes a problem particularly for very faint Auroras which can hardly be seen at the best of times. See Plates 4, 33–35. Twilight and dawn take their toll of auroral displays as I have already described (see Plate 63) but they can be coped with and are more of a problem during the spring to autumn time-frame.

It will be very noticeable from the range of photographs reproduced in this book that colours vary enormously and it is important that the time of year and time of day are carefully considered in addition to the different qualities of light, air temperature and atmospheric conditions (eg frost haze, humid air, dust levels etc) which probably all play a part in affecting the colour of the Aurora captured on the film. In my notes on photography I am at great pains to stress that my methodology is uniform and involves as little interference with the exposure of the film as possible (eg no filters).

In concluding this section and before allowing the reader to indulge in the following pages of photographs of Aurora displays from around the world, I would summarise the previous discussion as follows.

The Aurora probably occurs far more commonly than most people realise and can be seen over most of Scotland and even in England when the displays do occur. The best way to see the displays is to look out on dark clear nights, on a regular basis, from August and through to early May, to the North. There is no requirement to have expensive equipment – even binoculars are not very much use; the best way to see and enjoy these unique and spectacular displays is with the unaided human eye.

Even bearing in mind that most of the displays will not be as colourful as the many photographs in this book, there will be, I can assure the reader, no sense of anti-climax when you see your first active Aurora display; its scale and highly active movement will be awesome. If you are lucky enough to see a powerful Corona display when all the colours can be seen with the human eye, then the experience will be unforgettable – I do not think there is anything else occurring in the night sky to compare with the enormous scale, colourfulness and beauty of such a display and this combination makes it perhaps one of the few peaceful, yet spectacular, events that occur in Nature which will never be forgotten once seen. The photographs that follow can only hint at the scale and suggest only limply at the spectacle that awaits you when it happens for you.

**1 Aurora behind
Crathes Castle**
9 October 1990, 22.45

The way to make your Aurora photograph more interesting is the use of a recognised local landmark, in this case the most visited Grampian property of the National Trust for Scotland, Crathes Castle on the River Dee near Banchory. A little moonlight helps to add definition to the castle and makes the gilded weathercock gleam as well. The flag flutters in a light breeze.

17

2 Auroral Glow
The Neuk
9 October 1990, 00.35

The morning before the Crathes Castle Aurora, this unusual light level towards the North, where one would expect normal darkness, is often the earliest sign of pending auroral activity.

3 Aurora Arc
Cairn O'Mount
26 December 1989, 22.00

The Arc commonly appears as a silvery band of pale whitish light sitting to the North and is the usual sign of auroral activity about to start. On very rare occasions it can last a whole evening with no activity, but usually activity follows within an hour or two.

4 Aurora Arc in Moonlight
Crooktree
30 August 1991, 00.25

Strong moonlight make auroral displays less visible but once eyes have become dark adjusted then this classic sign is easily identified, as is the local countryside as the very sensitive higher-speed film illustrates.

5 Aurora – Double Arc
Crooktree
7 March 1994, 20.15

Where the Double Arc occurs, it appears to be an early sign of a very powerful auroral display, as was the case on this particular evening. See plates 68-73.

6 Aurora – Single Ray
The Neuk
25 January 1990, 01.30

This photograph captures a single ray, extending upwards from the Arc and also clearly shows even on a static image the broad band created by the lateral movement captured over the 40 second exposure time for the film.

7 Aurora – Multiple Rays
Cairn O'Mount
26 December 1989, 23.15

As the auroral display increases in power several rays can commonly be observed extending from the arc, often all exhibiting lateral movement in unison, and reaching different heights into the night sky.

8 A Strange Single Ray
The Neuk
19 February 1990 20.50

This was an unusual, single ray without any apparent contact with an arc or any other auroral activity visible, although it might have been hidden beneath the extensive cloud cover. It was unlikely to be a security light as it was seen several miles away to the West at the same time.

9 Single Ray
The Ley
1 May 1990, 01.52

This single ray was part of a continuing sequence of activity as can be seen from the other plates starting at Plate 55. The encroaching dawn light gives the violet colouration.

10 Aurora at Full Power
Cairn O'Mount
26 December 1989, 23.20

Viewed from over 1,000 feet altitude on the northern slopes of the Cairn O'Mount, this was near the point of maximum activity for this particular Aurora. See earlier plates 3 and 7.

11 Green Aurora
The Neuk
15 February 1990, 23.00

A common and often visible colour to the human eye – the green aurora is evidence of activity at low level exciting oxygen molecules. As the activity and power of the display increases, higher level gases especially oxygen come into play, as in the following plate.

12 Green and Red Aurora
The Neuk
15 February 1990, 23.15

Very common colours, although not always visible together to the human eye, is the gas energised at low and high levels and in the case of oxygen the most common gas, giving the green and red colours. Red is by far the most visible and common colour the author has seen over the years.

13 Folded Green Aurora
Crooktree
7 March 1994, 20.27

The folded bands of this predominantly green aurora was the most active evening of activity which occurred over seven days. This folding creates one of the displays often referred to as 'like curtains or drapes' because of their obvious similarity to hanging household curtains. They are also very like the early paintings of the Auroras depicted by the early explorers of the Arctic and Antarctic regions. See plates 68-73.

14 Patching
Crooktree
11 May 1992, 00.30

Pulsating patches or 'surfaces' of light which appear from nowhere for a few moments – they seem to be switched off and on, and in different parts of the sky as well. Often they occur after the main Auroral activity has finished. See also plate 25.

15 Streamers
The Neuk
21 March 1990, 01.00

Usually very active and quick moving, these laterally moving rays seem to have bases which flare off with intense light, like smouldering paper does when fanned with fresh oxygen. They also do not seem to be attached to a defined arc as say in plate 7.

16 Shimmering
Crooktree
18 October 1995, 22.00

Similar to patching, these bands of light seem to hover in the sky with no obvious attachment to arc or auroral display. Flaming which often occurs towards the end of a major Aurora have proved impossible to record on film and would appear to be much lower in power, and exist for much shorter periods than the shimmering or patching forms.

17 Corona at Inchmarlo
Near Banchory
3 October 1991, 23.40

The most powerful displays, especially over the UK, are characterised by the Corona. This photograph shows one of three frames capturing this sudden and very short-lived (lasting for all of three minutes) burst of a 'blood-red' auroral corona appearing eerily above a local forest. Tom McEwan also managed to obtain some beautiful slides of this display from his home in Ayrshire.

18 Green Corona
North Dakota, USA
21 August 1991, 12.40(MDT)
Photo: Jay Brausch
50mm f1.9 for 40 seconds

A very unusual colour for this coronal vortex and although very characteristic of the shape of an UK coronal apex, the normal colour observed by the author is red. Other colours of a pastel hue have been observed, eg plate 21.

19 Red Corona
Crooktree
26 February 1992, 20.15

A more common colour of the coronas in UK skies. The dome-like apex in typical red colour often with arms cascading down towards all the horizon in all directions. See plate 23 for a different colour of a corona in Finland.

20 Ghostly Corona
Crathes, near Banchory
25 March 1991, 23.55

Set against Crathes Castle the rays from this Corona create a ghostly shape in the night sky – it is easy to understand the cause of many folk-tales of spirits and demons in ancient times, such as Viking or Eskimo legends.

21 Corona Crown
Crathes Castle
25 March 1991, 23.50

This photograph was taken looking directly upwards to the apex of this dome-like centre of the corona and the previous photograph was a continuation downwards towards the horizon. A less usual colour to the more common red ones that follow.

22 Corona (Fish-eye)
Crooktree
2 February 1992, 23.50

This 360° view using the Sirius/24mm lens combination gives a clear impression of the coverage of the night sky with a coronal display.

23 Corona (Fish-eye)
Turku, Finland
17/18 November 1989
Photo: Pekka Parviainen
Fuji RSP at 800asa f2.8 for 10
seconds

This beautiful Finnish Corona has been spectacularly photographed using a 8mm f2.8 fish-eye lens. A very striking combination of colours set off against the peculiar black space.

24 Aurora and Broken Cloud
Crooktree
16 August 1991, 00.30

One of the most common frustrations for the UK Aurora watcher is the lack of clear skies, with clouds being the most usual problem – timing is crucial as can be seen with the photograph on plate 50.

25 Aurora and Ursa Major
Crooktree
29 August 1991, 23.46

Probably the most distinctive of the northern star groupings is that of *Ursa Major, also* known as The Plough, the Great Bear or Big Dipper. It is a good marker for looking for the signs of an early Aurora and in this case some patching was the early sign of an Arc which later went active. See plate 4

26 Red Corona and Cassiopeia
Crooktree
26 February 1992, 21.30

A 24mm wide-angle lens is completely filled with this red light from a full Corona over Deeside. The display had become active around 19.15 but was later hidden by cloud at 20.45 for the rest of the evening. The constellation of *Cassiopeia*, like a 'w', is clearly visible on the right – just join up the five dots!

27 Coronal Arms
Crooktree
2 February 1992, 23.55

Like a ghostly apparition, the sweep of the corona's rays stretch upwards into the night sky with an eastern aspect.

28 Strong Rays
Pascoag, Rhode Island, USA
16 June 1991
Photo: David A. Huestis
5Fuji RHP(400) 20sec
exposure/Konica 50mm

An Eastern USA Aurora taken from David's current home and from an area not usually associated with auroral displays. See another of David's studies from a different part of the eastern USA, plate 43.

29 Author's First Aurora
27 September 1989, 00.30

This was the author's first Aurora captured on film. After a long wait, the cloud cover eventually cleared and the Aurora was photographed on the hills at Heatheryhaugh, Glen Dye on the Cairn O'Mount road. Patience rewarded.

30 Corona and Orion
Crooktree
26 February 1992, 19.20

This Coronal display was active immediately after dark and being so powerful, it is possible to include the constellation of Orion, to the south, in this 360° study using the Sirius/24mm wide angle lens which captures the almost total coverage of this Coronal display.

31 Aurora and Pleiades
The Neuk
15 February 1990, 23.20

A very famous and easily identifiable star cluster (M45) towards the west, captured against the rays from this very active display which had started with very strong folding of the arc around 21.15. This was RSP film rated at 800asa. See plate 39 for a comparison using negative film.

32 Corona and Orion
Crooktree
26 February 1992, 21.33

A clear illustration of the strength of a display for observers in the northern regions is to see an Aurora set against Orion, probably the most well known of the constellations when looking south. In this case it is still the Corona from two hours earlier as shown in plate 30.

33 Aurora and the Moon
The Ley
30 April 1990, 23.10

The Moon adds extra interest to this Aurora but does not dampen down the strength of the Aurora too much. As the evening's activity progresses, the next plate shows the Moon dropping and the strength of the auroral display growing. See plate 55 onwards for several photographs of this very active night.

34 Aurora and the Moon
Harestone Road
1 May 1990, 01.10

35 Aurora in Moonlight
Banchory
11 April 1990, 00.35

After an evening of active but generally faint displays against the light of a full moon, this sudden appearance at just after midnight (GMT) was photographed from the back door. It is not diminished by the obvious urban light pollution or the light from a full moon directly behind the photographer.

36 Horseshoe Display
Kemnay, Aberdeenshire
11 April 1990, 00.30
Photo: John MacNicol
Fuji RHP 40 secs 55mm lens

John was also up Aurora watching – we keep each other advised and he obtained this very distinctive horseshoe-shaped Arc some 20 miles north of my position, but with less of the light pollution.

37 Corona over Large City
Aberdeen
20-21 October 1989, 20.00
Photo: Steve Graham
Fuji RHP(400)Pentax K1000
28mm f2.8 for 15 seconds.

This spectacular burst of red from a Coronal display was photographed by Steve from the western side of the city of Aberdeen and is indicative that Aurora can be seen from urban areas, especially after eyes have become accustomed to the dark.

38 Aurora and The Plough
The Neuk
25 March 1991, 22.15

With the obvious *Ursa Major* star group, The Plough, the 24mm lens is full of the glorious red associated so often with coronal aurora displays. This one to the north of Crathes Castle preceded an evening of very active and ever-changing coronal colours. See earlier plates 20 and 21.

39 Pleiades to the West
The Neuk
15 February 1990, 23.23

These large rays are stretching well to the west of this site and include the Pleiades. This very strong display has showed up well on the Fujicolor 1600 negative film although I found it less effective on lower light subjects such as Comet Hale-Bopp. See also plate 31, the same display on slide film.

40 Aurora on Kodak
The Neuk
24 January 1990, 21.30

The trail of a passing aircraft – heading West – disappears as the shutter is closed. This was taken on Kodak Ektachrome 800/1600asa slide film rated at 1600asa. See plate 42. The aircraft can be seen passing through a cloud on the right and the little dots on the line are the strobe lights.

41 Aurora from Spacelab 111
May 1985
Photo: R. Overmyer/NASA

A very different viewpoint for an Aurora – over the top of it. The red tops to the rays are clearly visible and is illustrative of the many astounding photographs to have been captured by the Spacelab/Challenger missions of recent years.

42 Aurora on Fujichrome RSP
The Neuk
24 January 1990, 21.20

As mentioned in plate 40, another air-craft adds an extra dimension to this Aurora photograph taken on Fujichrome RSP slide film, rated at 1600asa. These were part of early cross-checking of the various films' character-istics and although there is little per-ceivable difference, the author used the Fuji for all his future Aurora pho-tographs.

43 Aurora over Massachusetts, USA
17/18 September 1979
Photo: David A. Huestis
Ektachrome 160 (@400) Konica 50mm
20secs

Another one of David's eastern USA studies, this one a dawn photograph capturing the red tinge of this strong display. David organises an Aurora Alert Hotline from his home at Rhode Island; but nice to see your own as well. See Plate 28 for the display caught more recently near his home.

44 Corona Over Hopeman
Elgin, Moray.
21/22 October 1989, 20.00
Photo: Richard Pearce
Fuji RHP400 28mm f2.8
20–30secs

This rich deep red Corona was captured by Richard on the coast near Elgin and has already been published as the cover photograph of the first edition of Neil Bone's excellent book about the Aurora. (His latest edition is recommended for all those who wish a deeper understanding of the Aurora.)

45 Aurora over England
21/22 October 1989
Photo: Brian Sidney
400 Chrome 28mm f2.8 20 secs.

Occurring on the same night in October as the previous photo, an interesting illustration that displays seen as a Corona in Scotland will be strong enough to be observed as far south as mid England. This one of Brian's is taken near Cramlington in Northumberland.

46 Aurora
Southern Scotland
8/9 November 1991, 00.55
Photo:Tom McEwan
Fuji RHP400 50mm f1.8 40 secs

This red aurora taken by Tom near his home at Glengarnock, Ayrshire, contrasts with the green colours of the next plate taken on the same night but further south in England.

47 Aurora in Northumberland
8/9 November 1991
Photo: Brian Sidney

This green aurora display taken on the same evening as Tom's hides a further secret. The scale of this aurora is captured on a 20mm lens with an identifiable *Cassiopeia* at the top right and at the bottom left the huddled figure of Brian – that gives me an idea for using some of the Standing Stones.

48 Aurora and Comet
Crooktree
17 April 1996, 23.00

Arriving as it did during the lowest level of auroral activity the addition of an Aurora display to the exceptional presence of Comet Hyakutake was a great event and the author's luck continued for the appearance of Hale-Bopp as the next two photographs will show.

49 Aurora and Comet
Crooktree
28 March 1997, 23.20

The very spectacular Comet Hale-Bopp could not be allowed to pass unrecorded without an Aurora display although this was a very poor display and was interrupted earlier in the evening with much cloud cover. A faint ray is discernible just beneath the Comet. *Cassiopeia* is clearly visible above the Comet. Not to be out done the author also got the Comet with a falling meteor – sadly not all three together.

50 Aurora and Comet
Crooktree
11 April 1997, 00.50

Another bite of the cherry, but this time with the clouds proving equally frustrating as this photograph clearly shows. The Comet has just cleared the cloud bank but as the Aurora has decided to wane. Some rays are visible on the right, tipped with a delicate hue of violet. For more detail about these colours see John's discussion in his scientific section.

51 Auroral Pennants

North Dakota, USA
31 August 1991, 22.00 (MDT)
Photo: Jay Brausch
50mm f1.9 lens for 40 secs

A very unusual structure of activity from an Arc with a form and colours never observed by the author in Scotland. The stars visible are Attair (on right) and the constellations Delphinus (the Dolphin) and Sagitta. Jay lives in Glen Ullin which is situated at latitude 46.8°N. Deeside in Scotland is situated 57.1°N.

52 Triple Arcs

North Dakota, USA
6 November 1991, 01.00 (MDT)
Photo: Jay Brausch
28mm f3.5 for 30 seconds

The rich folding of this triple arc is similar to that of the author's taken in March 1994 (see plates 13 and 72) but lacking in the scale of this spectacular display. Jay remarks that this display only lasted for around 2 1/2 minutes.

53 Aurora Rays
Turku, Finland
2/3 May 1990
Photo: Pekka Parviainen
Fuji RSP at 800asa 24mm f2
for 5 seconds

The classic rays giving low (green) and high (red) oxygen colours but with very different hues to those of the author taken in Scotland as shown on plate 12. *Cassiopeia* is almost dead centre.

54 The Arc Goes Active
The Ley
30 April 1990, 23.28

The beginning of a busy night which is captured on the next six plates. The evening had already got under way earlier as shown on plate 33.

55 Arc with Streamers
The Ley
30 April 1990, 23.30

The Arc from the previous photograph is viewed more to the West and as the activity intensifies rays are seen streaming from beneath the main arc appearing to come out of nothing just above the distant Hill of Fare. Note the colour differences and again noticeable in the next plate.

56 The Ley Tree
The Ley
1 May 1990, 00.40

Into a new month by a few minutes and the auroral activity continues to intensify, here framing the Ley Tree with 'flames' that do not burn! A convenient forestry loading pull-off made this a safe position to keep off the road, and the tree and nearby telephone poles useful compositional tools. A little further along the road was The Neuk, another favourite viewing spot of the authors'.

57 Folding Arc
The Ley
1 May 1990, 00.45

As this particular display neared its most active stage, the arc curved round on itself whilst the rays extended upwards. *Cassiopeia* features clearly in the centre of this photograph which was when the author ran out of film - not a time for celebrating as the Aurora climbed to its crescendo.

58 Pink Lipstick and Larch Tree
Harestone Road
1 May 1990, 01.15

After returning with fresh film, the ten-minute gap did not appear to have cost me much, as the activity levels were as intense as when I left. This huge ray was towering above a mature roadside larch - the branches in the photograph are some 20 metres high. The colour was not visible to the degree shown here - it is often the case that these very sensitive films enhance the colour as well as show up colours not even guessed at when watching with the human eye.

59 Streamer under The Larch
Harestone Road
1 May 1990, 01.25

The auroral activity continued unabated and I watched and photographed as several rays seemed to flare brightly at their bases as this sequence of the display died down. The larch tree made a suitable composition and this photograph later became a successful J. Arthur Dixon postcard

60 Arc Active Again
The Ley
1 May 1990, 01.35

After a short lull, another Arc appeared, strengthened and burst into activity with several faint rays appearing. The final sequence of this display lasted until dawn but overall it was not as powerful as the earlier period.

61 The Ley Tree and Large Ray
1 May 1990, 01.51

Sometimes one distinct ray will break from the arc and this suitably set off. The Ley tree. In plate 9 the start of this active period can be seen, while in this picture the ray has expanded and is moving westwards – to the left. The violet colour is due to the increasing dawn light.

62 Dawn Light Takes Over
The Ley
1 May 1990, 03.00

Dawn light from the east (right side towards Aberdeen) increased in strength and with it the auroral display was drowned out, and although it appeared to be continuing to be very active, eventually became impossible to see. Time to go home to bed.

63 The Great Aurora Over Aberdeen

12/13 March 1989, 20.00–21.25
Photo: Steve Graham
Ektachrome 400, Pentax K1000
28mm f2.8 15 seconds.

Steve has captured the power of this huge Corona, a display so powerful that it was seen in Bermuda. The now named 'Great Aurora' was so powerful that there was no difficulty in seeing through any city light pollution.

64 Aurora Over Edinburgh

30/31 March 1989
Photo: David Gavine

This Aurora photographed from David's home in Edinburgh is another illustration that Aurora can be seen against the odds both of the more southerly latitude and the extreme light pollution of the Capital City. The effects of the City lights can be seen with the very orangey colour cast on this photograph – a feature of artificially lit daylight balanced film.

65 Double Arc
Upper Craigton
5 March 1994, 22.20

The lower quality Aurora of this evening signalled the beginning of seven consecutive nights of auroral displays, the best of which was on the night of 7 March as the next plates show.

66 Early Morning Display
Crooktree
7 March 1994, 00.46

The faint activity disappeared shortly after this photograph, followed by increasing cloud and wind – not a good omen for the night to come.

67 Double Arc – Evening
Crooktree
7 March 1994, 19.45

First sign of another evening of possible activity was foretold by this double arc. See plate 5 for it at a slightly later stage, after it had waned and then grown in intensity a further time.

68 Aurora Display Begins
Crooktree
7 March 1994, 20.20

The fish-eye Sirius lens captures the double arc as it goes active and the first rays begin to appear. The trees that feature in this photograph and the next two have a bearing of 285° – almost west.

69 Rays Increase
Crooktree
7 March 1994, 20.23

The simple composition of the trees is used to effect in this photograph and in the next one to give depth to the display and a sense of scale to the increasing height of the rays, captured best in the upright format.

70 Arc Fades
Crooktree
7 March 1994, 20.24

As the arc fades more rays are appearing which seems to be the usual pattern. Although for the next frame, the quick and simple expedient of turning the camera to the landscape allows the capture of the enlarging auroral display. In the space of minutes the display can take on many forms and in this case areas to the right (ie the north) begin to become active as the western aspect declines.

71 Folded Green Arc
Crooktree
7 March 1994, 20.28

The activity has now moved to the north (magnetic north over right-hand tree) and the arc has started to fold and bend, and with the movement of several rays and flaring off of rays beneath the arc this spectacular display reaches its peak of activity.

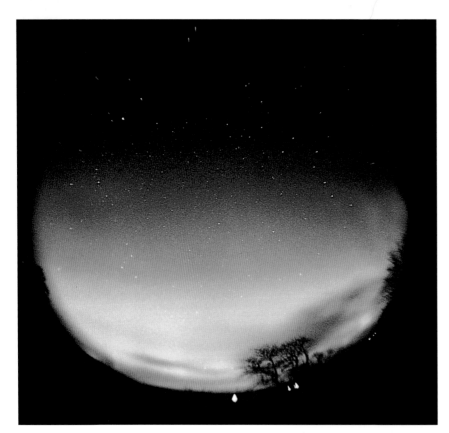

72 Fish Eye Aurora
Crooktree
7 March 1994, 21.00

This 360° view of the Aurora –
another burst of activity
shows the spread of this 'new'
display and it continued until
around midnight when it died
down. On following nights
through until 15 March displays occurred although never
to the intensity of the one
shown in the preceding photographs.

73 Single Ray
Crooktree
8 March 1994, 22.17

Not quite as spectacular as the preceding
night. I decided to make use of my Bronica, a
medium format camera. This single high ray
was taken using the 75mm (standard) lens at
f2.8 for 40 seconds and the Fuji RHP 400 was
pushed to 800asa (1 stop). Looking due
north, with *Cassiopeia* high on the left edge.

74 Aurora Over Greenland
March 1984
Photo: Clive Johnson
Olympus OM1 50mm Kodak
64 45 secs.

This unusual display was captured by Clive from Sondre Stromfjord on the west coast of Greenland. Probably the increased power level of this aurora has allowed an image to be seen on this very slow film. In practice only the most powerful displays could be photographed in the UK on slow/medium speed films.

75 Auroral Bands Over Alaska
Photo: Lee Snyder
1977

The tremendous power levels and scale of the most commonly photographed auroral displays are well illustrated in this stunning photograph by Lee and part of the excellent slide packs from the Institute of Geophysics of the University of Alaska in Fairbanks.

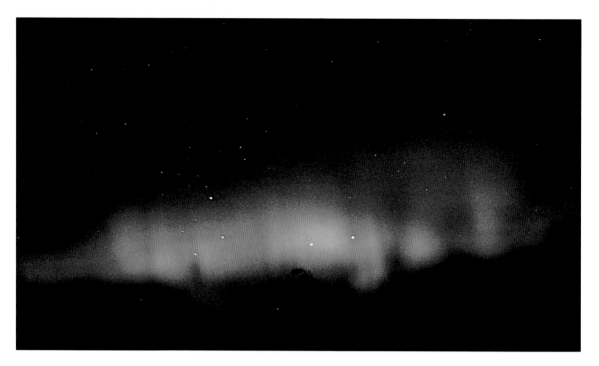

76 Aurora Australis
22 October 1981, 14.00 UT
Photo: Martin George
Agfa CT18 (50asa) 28mm f3.5
2 mins

Martin photographed this Aurora Australis display from Mount Nelson, which is near Hobart in Tasmania, Australia. The stars discernible above the tree outline are the inverted Southern Cross and Pointers (Alpha and Beta Centauri). This was part of one of the best displays ever seen in Tasmania and was even seen in the city centre of Hobart.

77 Aurora Australis
17 April 1990, 11.10 UT
Photo: Martin George
Fuji RHP400 28mm f3.5 2 mins

This Aurora display was photographed near Relbia, south of Launceston, Tasmania and shows clearly the different colours from low and high oxygen. The bright star above the tree is Achernar, the brightest star in the constellation of Eridanus.

PHOTOGRAPHY OF AURORA DISPLAYS

In general photography of the Aurora is not a difficult thing and given the various pointers advised in the next few sections there is no reason why anyone cannot obtain photographs as good, if not better than those reproduced in this book.

When I set out to photograph the Aurora I always envisaged that I would wish to build up a thorough collection of auroral photographs based on as committed a study of them as I could practically make. I was not anticipating that the collection would become as extensive as it has partly because I was under that myth that auroral displays were very rare. As I started to photograph them and was gradually aware from reading what little literature that existed and gleaning further bits of knowledge from John MacNicol and his colleagues that I became addicted to the possibility of photographing the 'big one', the Corona to surpass all Coronas splashing the heavens with all the colours of the rainbow covering huge celestial 'curtains' like some dream episode in a sci-fi blockbuster – well, I have not yet captured that display but there is always next month or next year or the next peak in the eleven-year cycle!

I experimented in the early days of photographing Auroras using different films, exposure times and various filters and lenses and fairly rapidly decided on a combination of factors which I have applied since without any great change other than to change the length of exposure given the apparent power level of the particular display – a function of experience in the main. One general rule in photography is to standardise on a set of parameters, for example film speed, lens, exposure time etc, and then stick with it rather than continually changing and experimenting. This does not mean that you must always stand still - new films in particular are always being developed, increasing film speeds but not at the expense of grain so that modern film emulsions in the 400 to 1600 asa range are today almost as grain free as the medium films were ten years ago. Improvements are especially frequent in colour film technology.

The other factor I considered at an early stage was that as my collection of auroral photographs grew then if I wished them to be valued from a scientific viewpoint then any perceived changes would be a function of the auroral displays and other extraneous factors such as temperature, time of year or day but not reflected in any way with changes of the camera equipment or films.

And here is a point on the artistic aspect of the photography. I have tried to concentrate on the auroral displays most of the time but occasionally I have changed my viewplace to include a more interesting foreground, eg Crathes Castle or the Ley Tree near to Crathes. Something interesting in the foreground is always a useful element in landscape photography to add a sense of depth and perspective and Aurora photographs probably fit best into this category of compositional work.

It has however been my policy to work as much as possible in the same location to maintain the scientific strength of my collection so that, as much as possible, the large variety of Auroras photographed can be compared with as much 'controlled' elements as possible. One area I have not yet tried (and this is an ambition) is to photograph Auroras over water to see what reflected qualities might be observed.

The pointers described throughout the next few sections are for your guidance only. You may wish to experiment yourself as you should do and any self-respecting photographer will easily determine what elements they might need to change to suit their own equipment or favourite film. The photographs, unless otherwise stated, reproduced in this book have been photographed using the methods I have described as my 'standard' practice over the years.

THE CAMERA AND ASSOCIATED EQUIPMENT

Camera Body and Lens

In the main I have used 35mm camera bodies to photograph the Aurora, principally because I can get faster 35mm film emulsions then larger formats and because I get more exposures to a roll of film. In my early days the fastest medium format lens I had was a 75mm (standard equivalent to 50mm – 135mm lens) f2.8 Bronica lens and the fastest film I could buy was the Agfa 1000asa 120 chrome emulsion. In 35mm I had a 28mm wide angle lens and the sensible fast films were rated at 1600asa. Given the usual scale and spread of the auroral displays then, a wide angle lens seemed more useful and it was from this point that I started to experiment. See Plate 74 for Bronica/75mm lens study.

The second requirement of undertaking auroral photography was the length of exposure required and very quickly I found that even with the faster films of 1600 asa I was going to require long exposures of 30 seconds or more, even with the fastest lens I had – the f2.8. This aperture setting which is the widest open the iris of the lens will go is the setting which lets in most light. There are a few lenses available with faster apertures, eg f1.4 or f2, but these tend to be standard lens with their smaller area of view; the fast wide angle lenses are very expensive and on balance although they do offer some advantages for shorter exposure times one has to work within ones' finances. It is an ambition one day to purchase one of these fast wide angle lenses as obviously the shortest exposure times possible will give better records of the Aurora displays which after all exhibit considerable movement. I have recently bought a Sigma 28mm f1.8 and I have used it on the Comet/Aurora photographs (Plates 48–50).I was able to reduce my exposures times to 15–20 secs and when the strong auroral displays come again I would envisage much shorter times. See Pekka's Finnish studies – Plates 23 and 54.

Usually in landscape photography the widest aperture is that which gives the least depth of field ie the smallest depth in which a given plane is in sharp focus. In the case of the Aurora when they are usually the key subject matter to be photographed they are so far away that depth of field does not become a factor and the Nikon lens I normally use shows very little softness (out of focus) at the edges even when fully open. One notable exception was when I focused on my van bonnet to capture the reflections and ended up with an out-of-focus auroral display.

Having decided that I would have to undertake long exposures, the next important requirement was a camera which would allow me to undertake this. The most versatile of the 35mm camera bodies is the SLR or single lens reflex which allows the lens elements to be removed so that wide angle lens can be interchanged with standard or telephoto lens and so on.

The SLR is so-called because a mirror in the prism housing allows the image seen through the lens to be seen in the natural way through the viewfinder which the photographer looks through when framing the intended photograph. This method also allows for the focusing of the lens to be adjusted by turning the camera lens and the results observed directly through the viewfinder. The metering system may be a TTL metering system, designed so that the light level through the lens (TTL) correctly exposes the film given the combination of the film speed, the aperture setting and associated shutter speed which can be thus accurately calculated. On most of the older models and in particular the manual versions of SLR camera bodies most had the 'B' or bulb setting which

allowed the shutter mechanism to be manually held open for a given length of time and it is this that is vital for the type of exposures necessary for auroral photography.

In my case two of my Nikon camera bodies were the older manual cameras with this facility but the one I use most is a now obsolete Auto/manual body called a FG20. The advantage of this body was that the B setting could be operated with the meter battery turned off, and additionally that the B setting did not require battery power to work. On many of the more modern cameras the B setting requires battery power to operate them and that becomes an expensive and often very inconvenient aspect when you are having your camera sitting out for several hours on a freezing cold evening and then using it to take 30–40 second exposures. Camera batteries are very small and they do not last long under those kind of working conditions. If you have an old and more or less mechanical 35mm SLR do not throw it out – its most basic 'B' function is its most valuable in auroral photography: the ability to hold a lens and allow light to pass through the lens onto the film surface for a long period of time.

Compact cameras do not lend themselves very well to the task of photographing the Aurora, for very few have facilities for long exposures or are calibrated to take very fast films. If you are interested in photographing the Aurora then my advice would be to obtain a second-hand manual camera body with B setting and any reasonably fast second-hand lens from 50mm to 28mm lens. Then you can add the next ingredients – a locking cable release and tripod and you have all you need to photograph auroral displays. If you do not have a tripod then at a push get a bean bag (although it has been pointed out to me that the granular filling can settle and cause the camera to move), and find a suitable stone wall on which to prop both camera and bag; as long as you aim the camera in the right direction, checking to see neither bag nor wall is obscuring the bottom of the lens, then a careful exposure using the cable release can be undertaken.

Among other lenses I have used occasionally is my standard Nikon which has a fast aperture of f1.8 but obviously sees a much smaller area than my wide angle lens; it needs much shorter exposures than the wide angle sometimes even managing less than a few seconds on the cameras' auto-setting. I also use a 24mm Sigma f2.8 superwide angle lens when I observe particularly wide spread Aurora displays (Plate 26)

The other lens I have used to interesting effect is a Sirius Semi Fish-Eye which makes my Sigma 24mm lens a 360 degree Fish-eye lens but at fraction of the cost – though probably with a considerable loss of quality as well. It is most effective when a Corona is active as can be seen from those photographs reproduced at Plates 22, 30 and 69. I have now also acquired a 15mm Sigma Fish Eye f2.8 but have only had the chance to use it seriously on 14 April 1996 when photographing the Comet Hyakutake and an Aurora; also, as I mentioned earlier, I possess a new Sigma 28mm f1.8. Roll on some big Coronas.

The Locking Cable Release is necessary for holding down the shutter for 30–40 seconds; without it you are asking for camera shake however solid the tripod might be. An LCR is very inexpensive – under £5.00 – and allows you to press the shutter down with the cable button avoiding any camera shake. By engaging the locking/release flange the cable can be left for the length of the exposure, leaving you free to do other things like have a cup of tea, work another camera, look at the auroral display, check your timing source; then it is easily got hold of for the shutter to be released. (See B&W illustration below).

The Tripod is also another important element in taking good photographs. I use professional ones which tend to be very solid and heavy and this is particularly an advantage on windy nights. However any tripod is useful as it is important to support the camera which, as I have already indicated, is best left alone during the exposure. The slight movement or knock will probably not make too much difference as the exposures are so long anyway. The tripod is more flexible and is by far the best support for the camera as against the suggestion of using a bean bag on a wall – the wall is harder to move around! The tripod illustrated here is of a make which allows a camera to be pointed directly upwards, an important feature when photographing Corona, as you will see in the various examples shown in the colour plates. See Plates 19 and 21.

The last essential pieces of hardware are a watch with good clear second hands or a digital seconds counter, and, if they do not have their own built in light source, then a small penlight torch which can be used for viewing the watch face to keep a check on the time. A small torch is necessary to avoid any spill-over of light near the camera lens as well as not to mess up the night vision of the eyes. Another suggestion made to me was to cover the torch lens with a red filter, giving enough light to see the time source but not affecting your night vision. Lastly remember the notebook and pen for keeping notes of times when main events happened, film exposure and other details.

THE FILM

Having dealt with the hardware, the software is just as important for without it there would be no Aurora photographs recorded.

Colour

My early experiments covered the whole range of fast films, that was any films of 400 ASA rating or faster. During my first couple of Aurora displays in September 1989 I used several different makes of film in the three 35mm bodies I had, swapping the wide angle lens over to each one and doing a series of timed exposures from 1 second to 30 seconds, in stages of 10 seconds. Some of the ISO 400 films were push-processed to ratings of ISO 800 and 1600, and the two ISO 1600 films I tried were processed at 800 and 1600 ratings.

After some further experimentation I decided that I preferred the Fuji film RSP 11, a 35mm film capable of being rated at ISO 800,1600 or 3200. I preferred it at its 1600 rating (also called P2) and I have used only this film at that rating ever since.

I could see little difference in the grain structure of the film from ISO 400 rated films processed at their normal speeds or if pushed. Over the years when my slides have been reproduced in magazines or as postcards then if there was any grain

The author's usual set-up as described in the text: the Nikon FG20 with wide angle lens, used at full aperture, eg f2.8, a cable release with the locking plate which allows long exposures at the B setting for the shutter. The camera is on a sturdy tripod. With a strong Aurora and a faster lens, the FG20's Auto setting can also be used.

problem because of the film being so fast it was never intrusive or detracted from the vibrancy and impact of the photographs of the Aurora on show. A couple of comparative photographs filmed on Fuji and Kodak are included and illustrate that the differences are not great and that, as with most things, choice is often quite a personal thing in the final analysis. See Plates 40 and 42.

Subsequently I found out by accident just how advanced these modern 'fast' films are when I inadvertently exposed the 1600 RSP as if ISO 100 in the brightness of the Egyptian desert. On my return to Deeside my local processing laboratory pulled the film processing to the maximum and to my surprise I found the results were perfectly usable with hardly any grain problem of note – it appears that the ISO 1600 film emulsion is in reality a ISO 400 emulsion with some extra 'tweaking'.

In conclusion my experiments led me to a 'standard' formula of exposing my ISO 1600 film for 30–40 seconds using the 28mm wide angle lens at its widest aperture of f2.8. I have only adjusted this formula where I have been faced with particularly powerful auroral displays and felt that shorter exposure times would be necessary and have reduced the exposures to 30 or 15 seconds accordingly. On the rare occasion where I have chosen to use my standard lens (50mm) which is faster with an aperture of f1.8 then I have exposed for much shorter times and have even used the camera own automatic exposure system to get exposures of less than a second.

Finally… a health warning; the colour of these super sensitive fast colour films does greatly enhance the colour richness of the auroral displays recorded, often outwith the human eye's ability even to see the colours, so when viewing actual auroral displays there will not necessarily be a comparison with the photographs illustrated in this book.

Sometimes as I have indicated I have seen green and red, even in the lower strength displays, but it is only in the coronal displays that there have been either the rich reds, or the multi-colours visible to my eyes. People have differing sensitivities in regard to their eyesight and it is often the case that I have had colours reported to me that I have not seen, and on occasion neither have those colours been recorded on the photographs I have taken.

Black and White
I did some photography in B&W and generally based my exposure and other parameters on those described for colour. The films used have been ISO 400 HP5 (Ilford) and ISO 400 Tri-X (Kodak). In both cases the films were pushed for a couple of stops in Aculux (a Paterson developer) and although the results were acceptable they seemed to be more muted than the colour photographs. In pure terms the best results I obtained was using HP5 and processing it in Ilfotec HC for 14 mins at 20°C. The grain structure was very pleasing and one of those exposures taken on the Bronica medium format using the 40mm f4 lens was published in the *Grampian* title in the Photographer's Britain series (Alan Sutton Publishers).

I found in later experiments that I could retain the vigour of the colour slides by photographing them directly onto B&W film (inter-neg) and using PanF (a very fine grain film) processing them according to standard recommendations. This method allows the photographer to concentrate on the subject rather than operating two cameras with obvious possibilities of confusion and missing critical aspects of the displays. Making inter-negs also offers additional possibilities of controlling contrast as well as producing selective negatives of key points. In general however I view the photography of the Aurora as principally a colour medium exercise and B&W I feel is best left as a supplementary aspect, reproducible to publishing standard if required for the rare occasion required, and for this a good inter-neg is more than adequate. Experiments with faster T Max or Neopan are on the cards but not a priority in view of the above comments.

LENGTH OF EXPOSURE AND STAR TRAILING
One point that must be addressed in more detail is the length of time for the exposure. I have indicated previously that the compromise that I reached was an exposure time of 30–40 seconds at f2.8 using the ISO 1600 film rating. An exposure time of 1 minute I found in practice started to show clear signs of a problem called star trail; as the earth revolves and thus the camera 'fixed' to the earth by the tripod, the stars which are in a permanent position relatively speaking begin to lose their sharp pointed look and instead move on the film making a line. In certain circumstances this can be used to interesting creative effect but I find it unnecessarily distracting in producing the Aurora photographs that I do. I feel the shorter the exposure time, the more accurate is the record of the Aurora and that is my underlying goal.

If there would be any 'rule of thumb' applicable it would be the shorter the exposure the better as the Aurora displays are a moving phenomenon and thus any exposures of long duration are recording an averaging of this movement and that must be borne in mind looking at the photographs in this book. This is clearly noticeable in the photograph of a single ray illustrated in Plate 6.

In advanced astronomical photography, especially of distant galaxies or faint stars, exposure times are very long – sometimes tens of minutes even using ultra-sensitive film. The problem of this relative movement of the earth to the stars is solved by the addition of a motorised drive which moves the camera (as do the great telescope observatories) so that it is always pointing to the same point counteracting the movement of the earth. Given the premise above that the exposure times should be as short as possible then this sort of sophistication is unnecessary in photographing the Aurora. A better investment would be in a very fast (f1.4) 28mm lens – in excess of £2000!!

THE FUTURE

I fully expect to continue experimenting with both faster lenses and other fast films. One astronomer friend has told me he has been using Scotch Chrome 800 and has been very pleased with the results so that is certainly a film worth a try as will be the other 'new' fast films that regularly arrive on the scene. I would like to try a faster wide angle lens to overcome the one problem mentioned before – that most of my photographs of the auroral displays do not accurately capture them because many of the photographs, particularly of very active rays, are in a sense 40-second time slots of something that is in reality moving quite vigorously. A faster lens may mean that the ray itself is more sharply defined and the colours too might not be quite so garish as they appear in these longer exposures. See Plate 54 for Pekka's 5 second exposure.

I will however probably continue using the Fuji film indefinitely for the reasons I cited earlier about giving a consistency to my work over a period of time thus allowing photographs taken say in the next peak of activity to be readily compared with those taken during the last peak, knowing that many of the key elements have been kept the same. These will thus be my reasons for sticking to my formula and I hope I have given you enough to begin your endeavours effectively from this starting point, but that does not limit you to staying with them.

I am also interested in the aspects of digital imaging now making themselves available and at a price that is gradually affordable. And I would like to try videoing the displays – an area in which I have no experience but feel it would be worth experimenting with.

RECIPROCITY FAILURE

I must address myself to this particular aspect of photography as it is a characteristic of any time exposure photography.

In the exposure of any film there are certain built-in parameters for the film which mean that as long as it is exposed within the 'normal' tolerances specified by the manufacturer, then the exposures given are going to give acceptable results.

In the case of very long exposures, then the film's ability to respond goes beyond the norm and outwith its abilities to respond properly and record the details of the photograph. This is a particular problem with slower films faced with the cliché 'holiday sunset' where the camera meter might indicate a 1-second exposure but the reciprocity failure of the film will mean in reality that a 2-second exposure is necessary to get a correct exposure on the film. The manufacturers will indicate this aspect on the film's instruction leaflet. In the case of films like Fuji RSP 1600 this factor only comes into play after exposures of 30 seconds or so. I found this out several years after using the film consistently for exposures of 40 seconds or more.

The Correction Factor for Reciprocity Failure
The correction factor for this reciprocity failure was the addition of a green correction filter with a factor of 2.5, about the smallest correction possible. Subsequent tests by my film processor on prints taken from uncorrected slides, and with subsequent Aurora displays photographed using the correction filter, showed no discernible differences between the corrected and uncorrected emulsions. I have since not used the correction filter as it is one more element to go wrong especially when the lens and filter mist up because of temperature changes or increasing evening dampness.

Unfortunately with the latest versions of the Fuji Provia Professional RSP the reciprocity correction factor is now specified as requiring, for exposures over 16 seconds, colour compensating filters (CC) of 10M+5R and I will have to conduct some further experimentation to see if this has a noticeable effect on the colour balances shown in the films. I have subsequently approached Fuji about this matter and I quote from Kevin Langman, Technical Manager:

"The corrections that we do give for reciprocity compensation are generally comparatively small in terms of colour correction and filtration of changes of 2.5 to 5 CCs are as you see from the finished slides quite small to the overall effects, particularly on bright saturated colours such as those you are photographing. These changes would, of course, be more noticeable on a light neutral grey area but it would appear that this is not a colour range which frequently occurs in your photography.

"The use of correction filters, and indeed the use of extreme long exposures, should in my opinion not significantly affect the colour saturation or colour purity of the reproduction of Provia film."

As you look through the photographs in the book, you will see several from other photographers throughout the world and I have included any photographic information available. It is interesting to note the different films used eg Agfa for the Australis (Plate 77), Kodak 64 asa for the Greenland photo (Plate 75) which contrast with the generally faster films already discussed. I have also included a photograph taken from the Fujicolor Negative film (Plate 39).

OTHER POINTS ABOUT PHOTOGRAPHY

I have already mentioned other aspects of photographing Aurora which go beyond just the equipment and film but there are other smaller matters which sometimes get overlooked but which as I know to my own cost can ruin an evenings' work.

A spare camera and lens are handy if you have them, in case of the unexpected accident like the tripod being blown over especially on the tops of hills - I have had a camera damaged that way.

When setting up and periodically throughout the evening particularly if cameras are changed over or moved to new locations, or films are changed when finished, make sure that the two basic parameters are checked and set - the aperture and focus.

The aperture on the lens should be correctly set to the opening required - in my case usually f2.8. I once closed it inadvertently to f22 (its smallest opening and hence letting in the least amount of light) when I changed the camera onto another tripod and I didn't check it for a whole film of 36 exposures during the beginnings of a coronal display prior to moving to do the Crathes Castle exposures of 25March 1991.

Do not make assumptions; check every time and never allow the excitement of the moment to distract you from the job in hand - to take good photographs.

The other element to check is that the lens is focused to infinity - check it with the torch if you are not sure but usually it is at the point where the lens will not turn anymore - but that also applies to the minimum focusing setting as well so make sure you know which direction your lens turns to reach infinity. I have lenses which turn in opposite directions so a check with the torch is always advisable. As you are using the widest aperture with almost nil depth of view then the focusing to infinity is crucial. Small points and ones that are easily forgotten especially when that Aurora goes active.

For those whose cameras rely heavily on batteries then it is advisable to take plenty of spare batteries with you - keep them in a warm place; as I already mentioned if you can get a second-hand older mechanical camera that does not require batteries to work then that is the best bet. If you are a winter mountain photographer then the warmest place is usually in an inside pocket next to the 'heart'. When a camera is sitting in the winter night air in a freezing wind perched on a tripod and is expected to perform many long exposures then the batteries will not last long - if you do not have a spare with you, you are not going to get one at 1.30am in the back of beyond. Take plenty, not just one spare.

Another problem is that of the lenses misting up particularly on damp evenings when the temperature starts changing. Once your eyes are accustomed to the dark then you tend to spot this happening as you frame new views through the finder but if you are just taking a series of exposures from the same spot without checking the camera set up regularly then periodically check through the viewfinder or look at the lens itself with the pentorch to make sure all is well. Take plenty of dry tissues for drying off the lens.

I never found it a useful practice to take the camera and lens into the vehicle between displays - body heat tends to build up humidity and that is the surest way of getting lenses misted up. If there is a danger of rain or snow showers then a plastic bag draped over the camera loosely tied to stop it blowing away but left open to allow the air to circulate is the best way to keep the equipment dry yet easily uncovered when needed. You soon get used to working in the dark and get to know your equipment and where everything is, so that it is near at hand when needed. Apart from the focusing and aperture the other most critical thing is the proper loading of a new film - make sure the film has properly caught into the drive sprockets - use the car interior light to do this and always check once the camera is in place and your first photographs are being taken that the handle wheel on the camera outside above the film cassette is turning as you wind on the film for the next exposure or two. Keep in mind as you move towards the end of a film how many exposures are left - if you feel that a big auroral display is about to happen then it might pay you to fire off the last three or so exposures on a strengthening arc and have a fresh film loaded for the active display when it starts.

I only once ran out of film completely just when the Aurora went 'bananas' and I was some ten minutes drive from my reserve supply in the fridge at home - that was the time for crying, and kicking myself for having not taken enough rolls of film with me. The film is the most expendable element - take five rolls, use one and keep the rest in the fridge crisper for next time; take five rolls and use three when you have the fantastic Corona with all the folds and colours you have ever dreamed of and you will be a Happy Photographer; take one roll only and run out half way through and you will for ever hate yourself.

The Aurora you will see and photograph will be unique - you only get one chance; you will see others but they are all different in some respect and for the sake of an extra roll of film it will not be the occasion to try to save a few pounds.

SAFETY AT WORK

A point or two on safety. Let someone know what you are up to especially if you are new to an area and it is off the beaten track. Beware where you park - not near steep embankments or rocky ledges over tree covered burns etc - remember you will be moving around in the dark. Be obvious about what you are doing - it is not some big secret - but a local farmer or gamekeeper might take a different attitude if they find a lonely figure hunched up in a forest clearing at 2.00am in the morning. If they know you, and know what you are about on a regular basis then it can be to their advantage as well - a sort of scarecrow to the less welcome night-time visitor.

I never saw any human visitors to worry about throughout the many nights I was by the roadside although I did get a visit from the local police, once, around 1.30am - it was a friendly visit and I was glad that they were around although I must have looked a little stupid standing by the roadside with my hands over my eyes shielding them from the oncoming car headlights!

Certainly a warm drink is a must on those long cold winter nights although these days I tend to photograph from the back door so nipping inside between displays to make a cup of tea, or nipping out between the adverts to see if anything is brewing up outside is now rather a luxury. When I used to sit in my van a few miles from home from anything after 7.00pm through to 1am or 2am the next morning then the van had to be home. There is, though, a certain cosiness that creeps in on cold winter's nights, drinking hot tea or coffee from the flask, music playing and warmth from the vehicle's heater - not very environmentally friendly but necessary if you weren't going to freeze to death. It is important however to make sure you keep the windows partly open - closed vehicles and engines running for warmth can be dangerous, quite apart from the propensity to doze off and miss the main auroral display - no I never did that, I think.

The alternative which I still need now even though I can operate from the back door is good warm clothing; the great advantage of the modern day mountaineering or offshore industry survival gear is that there is plenty to choose from - insulated everything and in the winter you need it. I find woollen gloves with the finger tips missing are ideal for camera work and a good insulated anorak with padded pockets does the work of mitts. As your head is the area through which most body heat is lost then very warm headgear which doesn't get in the way of the eyes when looking through the viewfinder or get knocked off every time you bend down to look through it, is the best answer. Finally hillwalking boots and thermal socks for those hours of standing around often in snow with little exercise other than jumping up and down on the spot are absolutely vital to keep the feet warm.

Aurora watching is a waiting game but like a lot of sports when it goes active then there is little time to think about much else than the event and in this case for the photographer capturing that once in a lifetime event on film it is the utmost achievement. I hope I have covered most of the likely problem areas you might meet, but in the end your own knowledge, experience and common sense have to put the success of the venture totally in your own hands. I have given you a starting point, a benchmark; the rest is up to you. Best of luck.

SUGGESTED FURTHER READING

Astrophotography for the Amateur Michael
  Covington, 1985, CUP
*Observer's Handbook: Astrophotography: An
  Introduction* H.J.P. Arnold, 1995, Philip's

AURORAE (THE CAUSE OF THE EFFECT)

INTRODUCTION

The general description for an Auroral display is a glow along the horizon or curtains of coloured light.

A great deal of study on what causes the Aurora has been carried out over the last 3 centuries. An immense amount of research has still to be done to verify the exact nature of the high energy particles from the Sun and their interaction with the Earth's Magnetic Field and upper atmosphere. In the following pages I intend to briefly explain our current understanding of the mechanisms involved in creating one of the most awesome and yet most beautiful visual displays of nature in the skies of our earth.

Other Names for Aurora

The Aurora is more commonly named 'The Northern Lights'. Other names are 'The Polar Lights', 'The False Dawn' and 'The Northern Dawn'. In the North of Scotland the Aurora is also described as 'The Heavenly Dancers ' or 'The Merry Dancers'.

In the northern hemisphere Aurora is more generally known as the 'Aurora Borealis'. This name first appeared in 1649 in a book on 'Physics' by the French Astronomer Pierre Gassendi. The Italian astronomer Galileo Galilei used the term 'Boreale Aurora'. The word Aurora is the [Latin] for the word meaning 'Dawn', Borealis is also [Latin] for 'Northern', therefore Aurora Borealis means 'Northern Dawn'.

Auroral Displays are not confined to the northern polar regions of the earth. Displays can also be seen from Antarctica and South Island in New Zealand and on occasion Southern Australia and South America. When the Aurora is seen around the earth's Southern polar region it is termed 'Aurora Australis', Australis being [Latin], for Southern.

The Source of the Aurorae

The appearance of an Auroral Display has been attributed to many natural and supernatural sources during the history of mankind. Some of the causes were blamed on armies of supernatural beings fighting in the sky (Norse folklore). Light emitted from cracks in the earth or gases released from the earth. Sunlight reflected from snow in the Arctic snowfields or icebergs in the polar seas.

The inhabitants of Northern Europe, Russia, Alaska, Canada, Greenland and Iceland, have witnessed the fiery night skies for thousands of years. Stories have been handed down to the present day,

many telling of the mystical nature of the lights in the sky. The Greek philosopher Plutarch around 349 BC described features within an Aurora as containing 'Chasms (chasmata), trenches and blood red colours'.

THE SUN

Beware! Never look at the Sun directly through a telescope or binoculars, the magnified heat will burn your eyes permanently.

The Sun is a star around which the planet Earth orbits along with the other planets of our solar system. It is a large sphere of very hot hydrogen gas slowly converting the hydrogen into helium at its core using the process of nuclear fusion. The Sun is 1.4 million kilometres in diameter which is normal for an average sized star but gigantic when compared to the earth's 12,756 kilometre diameter and 1 million Earths could be placed inside the Sun. The Sun is of spectral classification G2V and is yellow in colour. Other stars in our sky appear as small points of light due to their great distances from us (billions of kilometres). Some of these stars can be as small as the Earth, or so large that if placed in the position of our Sun, they would swallow the orbits of all the inner planets of our solar system, namely Mercury, Venus, Earth and Mars.

On a summer's day and with a clear sky, we are all aware of the earth being bathed in the light and heat coming from the Sun. This energy travels to us, over a distance of just under 150 million kilometres. There are vast amounts of less noticeable forms of emission from our Sun and its ferocious surface than meets the eye. The visible part of the electromagnetic spectrum is only a small portion of the Sun's output. Visible light ranges from approximately 420 nm. to 700 nm. in wavelength (1 nm. or nanometre is equal to 1,000 millionth of a metre).

A closer look at the surface of the Sun would reveal a boiling ocean of very hot gases in what seems an eternal state of turmoil. The 'surface' of the Sun is a total misconception, rather like describing the top of the clouds as the 'surface' of the earth. The Sun has no known solid surface and is composed almost entirely of atomic and molecular particles. The Sun's surface layer is called the 'photosphere'.

The visible surface layer of the solar atmosphere appears as millions of rotating whirlpools of hot gas, arranged all across it's surface called 'cells'. The cells give a granular appearance to the Sun and in each cell or grain the hot gas is enclosed in a strong magnetic field. The size of each cell can vary but may reach around 1,000 km across. Cells are short lived features only surfacing for a few minutes before sinking to be replaced by another cell.

The Sun is not a stationary star, just like the earth it rotates on its axis but it takes 27.275 days at solar latitude 17 deg. to revolve (synodic period viewed from Earth) to 25.38 days mean solar rotation. Surface features near the poles take longer to rotate than equatorial features this is due to differential rotation of the solar atmosphere. The solar axis is also tilted by 7.25 degrees to the perpendicular plane of the ecliptic.

Sunspots

When a magnified image of the Sun is projected onto a suitable viewing surface, slightly darker patches can sometimes be seen. These patches or dark spots are termed Sunspots. A Sunspot is a slightly cooler area in the solar atmosphere. The outer visible solar layer or photosphere (sphere of light), has a temperature of 6000°K (degrees Kelvin). Sunspots may appear cold and dark but are still very hot; their dark appearance is only due to the contrast in surface brightness compared to the surrounding hotter gas and still radiate at around 4500°K. On closer examination Sunspots appear to have dark centres with lighter striated fringes surrounding them. The darker central area of a Sunspot is termed the umbra and the lighter fringe termed the penumbra. The striations surrounding the umbra is caused by the strong magnetic field lines visible in the penumbra. The majority of Sunspots appear as bi-polar magnetic pairs with positive and negative magnetic properties. Sunspots have extreme variations in size, ranging from a few tens to several thousand kilometres across.

Faculae

These appear as bright patches in the upper photosphere, they are associated with areas where Sunspot activity may form or has recently ceased.

Solar Emission

Solar Flares are one of the most powerful disturbances in the Solar atmosphere. Associated with Sunspot activity, they can form above Sunspot groups in areas of very strong magnetic field distortion. The resulting magnetic field reconnection produces an explosive release, of immense quantities of plasmatic particles in violent shock waves out into the Solar Corona this produces a Coronal Mass Ejection (CME). The duration of a flare may last from a few minutes to several hours.

Prominences

A Solar Prominence is usually visible as an immense arc of hot gas rising from the solar surface. The arc can extend for 100,000 km from end to end. Like a huge fiery rainbow it slowly rises until the arc either remains stationary for hours or days or breaks apart. Prominences are generally found where Sunspot activity has recently ceased. A prominence may erupt into a mass ejection of matter into the solar corona and out into the solar wind.

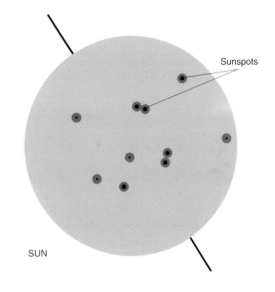

Solar Cycle

(periodic rise and fall in solar surface activity)
Surface activity on the Sun is not as steady and constant, as we would expect. Sunspot activity increases and decreases dramatically from 1 year to the next, in an almost rhythmic cycle covering an average period of 11 years. This period may vary between 8 to 16 years but averages out at 11.1 years. During each 11 year Sunspot cycle the number of Sunspots visible on the solar surface vary from small isolated patches to large groups of Sunspots visible to the unaided eye. The extremes of the Solar Cycle are named Solar Maximum for the period when maximum Sunspot activity is visible on the solar surface and of course Solar Minimum for the period for minimum Sunspot activity. The 11-year solar cycle is only half of a longer 22-year solar cycle. Since the solar magnetic field reverses from positive to negative over one 11 year cycle caused by stretching of the field lines through differential rotation, then from negative to positive over the second 11-year cycle (back to the start again).

The Solar Corona

Until recently the Solar Corona was only seen by the unaided human eye during a Total Solar Eclipse, when the Moon's disk passes in front of the disk of the Sun. For a few minutes at eclipse maximum the Solar Corona becomes visible as a bright glow surrounding the Sun. The temperature of the plasma within the Corona is estimated to be around 1 million° C. The reason for such a high temperature is as yet unknown. Observations by the Solar Polar Mission Spacecraft recently found the Sun to have no exact north and south poles instead it appears to have diffuse polar areas or zones.

Coronal Holes

Coronal holes are zones of open solar magnetic field connecting to space which allow particles to leave the Sun as high speed Solar Winds. They can release large quantities of hot plasma out into the solar system. When viewed using a narrow band filter displaying Hα (Hydrogen Alpha emission line), coronal holes appear as dark areas in the chromosphere.

The Solar Wind

Waves of plasma containing atomic particles constantly flow outwards in all directions from the upper regions of the Solar Corona this is called the *Solar Wind*. The particles within the plasma consist mainly of ionised hydrogen protons and electrons along with around 5% helium and small amounts of oxygen and other elements. The velocity of the high temperature plasma is great enough to escape the strength of solar gravity. The solar wind normally flows away from the Sun at a speed of 250 to 800km/sec and may reach 1000km/sec in storm conditions. This is far slower than the light waves and other forms of radiation which travel at or near the speed of light (300 000 km / sec). The solar wind draws upon the Sun's magnetic field, carrying the Solar magnetic field lines out into interplanetary space. This creates the *IMF (Interplanetary Magnetic Field)* consisting of plasma particles flowing along the IMF field lines.

Like all stars, the Sun is not stationary in space, instead it is on a perpetual journey around the centre of the Milky Way Galaxy. This journey takes about 230 million years to complete one revolution. Space within our galaxy is not empty, it contains an abundance of atomic and molecular particles. The density of this Galactic interstellar matter varies widely from around one to many million molecules per cubic centimetre. Possibly embedded within this molecular ocean is a weak galactic magnetic field consisting of weak interstellar fields within the local spiral arm . The Sun has to push its way through all of this as it moves along with its orbiting planets. The effect of this *Interstellar Wind* on the IMF surrounding the Sun is to distort the field into something resembling a comet, with the IMF pushed towards the Sun on the leading side forming a *Bow Shock* and the IMF behind the Sun being drawn into a long tail. The IMF reaches far out onto the solar system and has been detected by the NASA Pioneer and Voyager Spacecraft beyond the orbit of Neptune.

EARTH MAGNETIC FIELD

The Earth rotates on its axis causing the perpetual day and night cycle we witness during our lives. The physical North and South poles of the Earth are the points on the surface of the Earth around which the Earth rotates. The poles of the Earth's magnetic field do not correspond to the axial poles. The Magnetic North Pole of the Earth lies in Canada hundreds of miles from the Physical North pole.

The effect of this is to displace the magnetic latitudes of the Earth's land masses in relation to their geographical latitudes.

Earth's Magnetosphere

The planet Earth, like most large bodies in the universe, has a magnetic field. Just like a bar magnet the Earth has North and South Magnetic poles. The Magnetic Field of the Earth forms a protective shield around the planet called the *'Magnetosphere'* which defends the surface from being bombarded by most high energy particles and radiation from space and the solar wind. Magnetic fields are totally invisible to the human eye, but just like sprinkling Iron filings on a sheet of paper covering a bar magnet, to show the magnetic field lines, the earth can also display its magnetic field. Nature reveals the pattern of the earth's magnetic field every time we see a very active auroral display. Instead of Iron filings, highly charged gases emit light thereby showing the shape and movement of the magnetic field in the upper atmosphere.

The Magnetosphere is in no way a symmetrical envelope surrounding the Earth. The pressure of the solar wind on the sunward facing or dayside of the Earth pushes the magnetic field closer to the Earth's surface creating a *Bow Shock*. The Magnetosphere is stretched into a long tail on the night side or side facing away from the Sun called the *Magnetotail*. The overall shape is likened to a Comet with its long tail always facing away from the Sun or a ship moving through water creating a bow wave ahead of the ship and a long wake behind the ship.

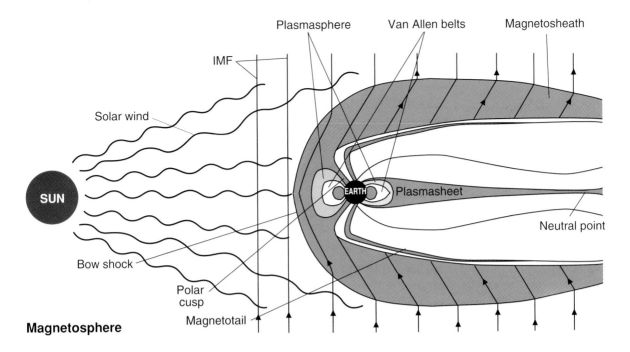

Magnetosphere

Labels in diagram: Plasmasphere, Van Allen belts, Magnetosheath, IMF, Solar wind, SUN, EARTH, Plasmasheet, Neutral point, Bow shock, Polar cusp, Magnetotail

Earth's Magnetopause

Earth's magnetic field lines in the outer layer of the Magnetosphere come into direct contact with the IMF and the plasma within the Solar Wind. This layer is called the *Magnetopause*. Solar wind plasma can transfer directly into the Magnetosphere and enter the polar magnetic field at the polar cusps.

The Auroral Oval

If you lived on the Earth's equator, you may never see an Auroral Display. There is a good reason for this. Photographs taken by the Dynamic Explorer 1 satellite (DE-1) in the 1980's showed the Aurora as oval rings of auroral light around both the North and South magnetic poles of the Earth. The ovals are not exactly centred around the Earth's magnetic poles. Along with the magnetosphere, the ovals are pushed by the solar wind away from the dayside or midday sector, toward the nightside or midnight sector of the Earth's magnetic poles. The ovals are almost a permanent feature of the Earth's polar regions. During times of high solar activity the ovals expand equatorially both in width and diameter into the more populated lower latitudes. Except for extremely rare occasions, the ovals never reach the equatorial regions of the Earth.

The Auroral Ovals are centred on the Geomagnetic North and South poles. The current position of the Geomagnetic North pole is situated in north-west Greenland near Thule, approximately 79° N, 70° W, and the Geomagnetic South Pole near Vostock in Antarctica. The Magnetic Pole (the

pole to which a compass points), is located 800 km South-west of the geomagnetic North Pole due to magnetic field distortions in the Earth's crustal layer. To add to all this the Geographical North pole is about 1200 km north of the geomagnetic North pole. The Ovals remain relatively stationary as the Earth rotates beneath them, with the midnight point reaching farthest south in the northern hemisphere and farthest north in the southern hemisphere. This midnight point is the best time to look for Aurora (approximately 22:00 hrs in the UK).

EARTH'S ATMOSPHERIC STRUCTURE

At first glance it would be difficult to judge the height of an Auroral display above the observers' head. Years of measurements from the ground, high altitude probes carried by rockets or balloons and more recently spacecraft, have lead to very accurate dimensions. The Aurora starts at around 105 km, above the earth's surface and extends up to 200 km but (may, on more rare occasions reach 1000 km). At these altitudes the atmosphere is very thin. Accurate measurements were achieved by the mathematician Carl Størmer (1874-1957) using Krøgness 10 × 14 cm glass plate cameras. The Krøgness cameras were suitably adapted for the frozen conditions of Norway. Around 40,000 photographs were taken during this survey; from this great photographic archive 12,000 were taken from two or more positions simultaneously to give height measurements.

Earth's Atmosphere Gases

We are aware of the air in the atmosphere by the fact that we breath it in and out of our lungs every day and the effects of the atmospheric winds. At sea level the air is quite dense (around 2.5×10^{19} particles per cubic centimetre) but as you climb above the mountains and clouds, the air gets thinner the higher you go. If you were to measure this density or pressure with a barometer the reading would start at around 1013 millibars, or 1 atmosphere, at sea level and slowly drop as you climb above the Earth's surface. At around 500 km the atmosphere contains around 7.3×10^{5} particles per cubic centimetre.

The gases we breath in the lower level of the atmosphere are mainly composed of nitrogen N_2 (78%), oxygen O_2 (21%) and the remainder comprising carbon dioxide CO_2 and other gases.

The atmospheric composition changes as we climb in altitude; at 80–100km and above, O_2 molecules in direct contact with ultraviolet radiation from the Sun through photodissociation are converted to Atomic Oxygen OI. The atmosphere gases at 100 km are N_2 at 76.5%, O_2 at 20.5% and OI at 3% – note that oxygen has increased in proportion to nitrogen.

The Ionosphere

Between 60 km and 400 km the atmosphere contains an abundance of positively charged (ionised) atoms and molecules along with negatively charged electrons; this is called the *Ionosphere*. It is divided into layers: the lowest, D Layer, peaks at 60 km, the E Layer at 110 km; the F Layer is subdivided into the F1 Layer with its peak at 160 km and F2 layer with a peak near 300 km. The proportion of ionised gases falls rapidly when in the nightside of the Earth's shadow but soon recovers when placed back into direct sunlight containing short wavelength UV and X-rays. Radio waves of wavelength 1–20 megahertz can be reflected from the F Layer for long-range communication. During Auroral activity the lower D Layer increases in density and begins to absorb radio waves therefore causing problems with radio communications.

Geomagnetic Storms

When an increase in the solar wind plasma reaches the Earth and enters its associated magnetosphere there is an increase in the intensity of Magnetic Ring Currents caused by field merging at the magnetotail. Particles are then injected into the Inner Magnetosphere enhancing substorm activity. Storms may last from a few hours to several days.

Auroral Substorms

Auroral Substorms are a daily occurrence and may last from 1 to 3 hours, the next substorm beginning as the previous one declines. This may continue to repeat over an entire 24 hours and beyond.

For the observer south of the auroral oval, East-west Arcs can be found to drift southward until they break up into highly active forms. An Auroral Substorm can be divided into 3 phases:

1. *The Growth Phase* The midnight sector of the Auroral Oval expands southward and grows brighter.
2. *The Expansive Phase* The Oval brightens from the midnight meridian both eastwards and westwards round to the noon meridian. Bright active auroral forms seen during what is termed Break-up.
3. *The Recovery Phase* Mainly patchy pulsating auroral forms general fading off.

STRUCTURE OF AURORAE

The visible structure and shapes seen in auroral displays have been divided into several well-documented types.

Patches

Luminous Patches not unlike moonlit clouds are sometimes found above the northern horizon. These are termed Homogeneous Patches and at times develop into other structures such as an arc.

Arcs

The Auroral Arc is in reality the leading edge of the Auroral Oval which is nearest to the observer. It is likened to a pale rainbow above the horizon and centred on the direction of the magnetic pole. The lower edge of an Arc is usually sharply defined as against the more diffuse upper edge. The sky is usually darker beneath the Auroral Arc than above, due to the contrast (this is the opposite from the true daytime rainbow in which the sky is lighter under the arc than above).

An Arc can remain stationary for hours or can slowly rise in height above the Northern horizon, and other features may develop along the length of the Arc such as rays or bands. At times of high auroral activity, two and more Arcs may be seen.

Rays

Vertical Rays can be seen stretching upwards from an Arc. They are in fact vertical folds in the fainter diffuse auroral glow above the arc. Rays can exhibit motion from East to West before local midnight or West to East after local midnight during the expansion phase of an Auroral Substorm. They may resemble a procession of vertical columns of light along the horizon. This possibly gave rise to the Norsemen's notion of an army moving across the sky.

Bands
When an auroral arc folds and twists like the folds in a ribbon, this is called Banding. Usually seen as activity increases.

Rayed Bands
A folded arc from which Vertical Rays stretch upwards giving the appearance of folded drapery is called Rayed Bands. Rapid movement and changes in structure may occur.

Corona
When the Auroral arc or bands pass above the observer they see a vortex or fan-shaped structure. This is called an Auroral Corona (*Corona* is the Latin word for 'crown'). The rays appear to rise from all around the horizon and converge to a point called the magnetic zenith (the angle is dependant on the observer's magnetic latitude). The observer is however witnessing an illusion of perspective due to the distance the rays reach high into the upper atmosphere. The usual comparison is to a road, railway or tunnel with parallel sides appearing to come to a point on the distance. The magnetic zenith in Earth's northern latitudes is the point in the sky to which the 'S' end of a dip-needle points. In Scotland this is several degrees south-east of an observer's True Zenith.

Pulsing or Flaming
Waves of light appear to sweep upward from the base of an arc or rays at very high speed (1/10th of a second from base to top), giving the effect of flames. This feature is usually seen during the break-up of an auroral substorm.

Flickering
An Aurora can sometimes appear to flicker causing rapid changes in brightness. This is usually only seen in the dying phase during very intense activity in the Auroral Zones.

Latitude and Auroral Displays
The Aurora is an almost permanent feature around the polar regions of the Earth. This is called High Latitude Aurora, but when seen from lower latitudes is termed Mid-Latitude Aurora.

Colour of Aurora
The different colours visible during an auroral display are produced by photon emissions by the various ionised molecules as they return to their neutral state at different altitudes within the upper atmosphere. Unlike sunlight which contains an almost continuous spectrum of colours, Aurora only produce light in a few very narrow bands in the spectrum.

Gases at normal sea-level atmospheric pressures emit light at different wavelengths from those emitted at the very rarefied levels found in the ionosphere and above. Listed below are some of the most predominant wavelengths emitted by the specific gas molecules during auroral activity. The list consists of the Atomic or Molecular Gas along with its colour, wavelength and respective height (altitude above the Earth).

Gas		Colour	Wavelength (nm)	Height (km)
Ionised Nitrogen	N_2+	Violet-blue	391.4	1000
Nitrogen	N_2	Violet-blue	427.8	1000
Atomic Oxygen	OI	Green-yellow	557.7	90-150
Atomic Oxygen	OI	Red	630.0	>150
Atomic Oxygen	OI	Red	636.4	>150
Hydrogen Alpha		Red	656.3	120

The lowest light level the human eye can perceive is in the green area of the visible spectrum and therefore Aurora emissions in the green OI line are among the faintest seen. An all-sky red Aurora can be seen when the magnetosphere is bombarded by mainly high energy protons from the Sun. Rays reaching up into the sunlight after midnight and near morning may appear violet or purple as they are enhanced by UV rays. Arcs and other auroral forms may appear green, yellow, red and even blue in colour. During a major substorm a wide variety of the above colours may be seen to mix and merge as different atomic molecules lose their unstable energy in the form of emitted light as they return to their neutral state.

OBSERVING AURORA
Although the light from an Aurora can often appear very bright in the night sky it slowly fades until it is drowned by the daylight sky. There are times when Aurora can be seen more frequently particularly after the solar Sunspot cycle maximum when Coronal Hole activity increases. The Earth's position near the equinoxes also appears to provide an increase in activity.

As has been mentioned the Aurora is best seen in geomagnetic latitudes above 60° and at least above

60° North and South of the equator, also away from bright town and city lights.

Recording Details

Noting down details of an Auroral Display can range from casual notes to very precise details for scientific records. If the observer keeps a personal record of astronomical observations the entry may be in diary form and consist of the fact that an Aurora was witnessed and the date on which it was seen. Due to the totally unpredictable nature of weather conditions in the temperate to polar regions of the earth's atmosphere, records of an auroral display can sometimes rely on just one or two people. It is not unknown for cloud to cover almost all of the regions in northern and southern continents of the earth.

If however the observer wishes to record detailed information on the appearance and behaviour of an auroral display the following notation can be of use. Other notation is normally used to describe the brightness and structure of an Auroral display and may be obtained from the addresses at the end of the article.

	Colour
Type A	green Aurora shading to red at top
Type B and E	green with red lower border
Type C	green Aurora
Type D	all-sky Red Aurora
Type F	blue-purple sunlit Aurora

More advanced records can be supported by photographing auroral displays. If accurate height measurements are to be found, the photographer should follow a standard recording procedure. Since the auroral structure being photographed is possibly at a great distance from the observer, a reasonable baseline for triangulation is required, at least 20 to 40 km. The auroral display may be 200 to 300 km to the north and at an atmospheric altitude beginning at 100 km and rising to 500 km. The use of standard photographic equipment greatly improves the scientific value of any photograph. A 35 mm TTL camera with a lens of either 50 mm or 28 mm focal length is best used along with colour film of ISO 400 rating.

Exposures taken at 15-minute intervals, e.g. 23:00, 23:15, 23:30 and 23:45, greatly improve the photographer's chance of corresponding with other photographers at distant locations. A record should be made of each exposure containing the date and time, exposure duration and direction of aim, e.g. North-east. For calibration of background starfield, record any bright stars or constellations in the field of view, e.g. Deneb in Cygnus or Capella in Auriga.

SOURCES OF FURTHER INFORMATION ON AURORAL ACTIVITY

Auroral reports for Northern or Southern hemisphere can be sent to the following addresses;

British Astronomical Association
Aurora Section,
Burlington House,
Piccadilly,
London,
W1V 9AG.

Royal Astronomical Society of New Zealand,
PO Box 3181,
Wellington,
New Zealand.

Related Internet Websites

With the advent of the Internet anyone with access to a personal computer with a modem and an Internet browser program such as Microsoft's Internet Explorer can access an immense amount of information on the subject of the Aurora. I have listed the best of the current websites available with up-to-date information on the status of solar activity, the solar wind and predicted Auroral activity. This is an excellent space weather-forecasting system from the world's leading research institutes and spaceprobes.

University of Alaska webpage
www.pfrr.alaska.edu

Northern Lights Planetarium Norway
www.uit.no/npt/homepage-npt.en.html

Current Solar Activity
www.sel.roaa.gov/

Suggested other reading:
The northern light: from mystery to modern space science Egeland, A., and Brekke, A., Endeavor New Series, 1984
Aurora: The northern lights in mythology, history and science Harald Falck-Ytter, Floris Books, 1985
The Aurora Watchers Handbook Neil Davis, University of Alaska Press, 1992
The Aurora Sun-Earth Interactions Neil Bone, Wiley-Praxis Series in Astronomy and Astrophysics 2nd Edition, 1996

© Copyright 1997 John MacNicol